Zaner-Bloser
HANDWRITING
A Way to Self-Expression

Blackline Masters
Grade 1

Senior Authors

Clinton S. Hackney, Ed.D.
Language Arts Consultant
Adjunct, Florida Southern College

Virginia H. Lucas, Ph.D.
Professor of Education
Wittenberg University

ISBN 0-88309-144-5

Zaner-Bloser, Inc., P.O. Box 16764, Columbus, Ohio 43216-6764
Printed in the United States of America

Table of Contents

TEACHER INFORMATION

I

Letter to Teachers

Clinton S. Hackney, Ed.D., co-author of Zaner-Bloser's *Handwriting: A Way to Self-Expression*, describes the contents of the Teacher Resource Binder.

Why Manuscript?

Introducing manuscript writing as a prelude to cursive is one of the most strongly supported practices in education. This article discusses the various reasons for the strong endorsement of manuscript writing by leading educational figures.

Classroom Organization

Many teachers agree that learning centers in the classroom provide valuable opportunities for extra practice and for expanding experiences as well as a place where you can meet the specific needs of individual students. This article includes suggestions for creating a useful writing/learning center in your classroom and answers such basic questions about writing centers as:

- **What** is a writing center?
- **Why** do I need a writing center in my classroom?
- **How** do I create a successful writing center?
- **When** is a writing center useful?
- **Where** would a writing center be most productive?

This article also provides teachers with instructions for creating handwriting grids on the chalkboard—a most effective tool for handwriting instruction.

Teaching Handwriting Through Modality Strengths

Students learn in different ways: the visual child learns by seeing (watching); the auditory child learns by listening and repeating what is heard; the kinesthetic child learns through hands-on experience. Learning characteristics of each modality are discussed in the Teacher Edition of *Handwriting: A Way to Self-Expression*, and activities appropriate for each learning style are provided. This article conclusively disproves the myth that, since it is essentially a kinesthetic task, handwriting cannot be taught effectively through other modalities. Hints and cautions are presented for each mode of learning to promote success in teaching handwriting to students of all learning styles.

Zaner-Bloser
EDUCATIONAL PUBLISHERS

Clinton S. Hackney, Ed.D.

LANGUAGE ARTS CONSULTANT

P.O. Box 16764 • Columbus, OH 43216-6764

Dear Teacher,

We believe that you will be just as excited about this Teacher Resource Binder as we were when we put it together for you. The contents were carefully selected to support Zaner-Bloser's *Handwriting: A Way to Self-Expression.*

In the pockets of the binder are various materials to make the teaching and evaluation of handwriting easy. These supportive materials are listed in Section III, along with a description of their use.

The first four sections in this binder, consisting of 64 pages, offer numerous suggestions for organizing your classroom, pacing your instruction, meeting special needs of children, and integrating handwriting with the other language arts. In Section V, you will find Practice Masters designed to accompany each page in the Student Edition. The page numbers are the same.

The School-Home Involvement Section, in both English and Spanish, provides parents with correct models of letterforms, illustrations of the pencil and paper positions, and other elements important to good handwriting. This information will encourage a consistency in the skills being taught at school and practiced at home.

We encourage your comments and suggestions.

Sincerely,

Clinton S. Hackney

Clinton S. Hackney, Ed.D.

WHY MANUSCRIPT?

Manuscript writing is taught to more primary grade children than any other style of writing. This popularity is a result of manuscript's ease of acquisition, legibility, and its relationship with other academic skills. In addition, it has great logical appeal to both supervisors and teachers. Most experienced teachers believe that the use of manuscript writing, rather than either cursive or some italic form of writing, is a better way to begin teaching writing.

EASY TO LEARN

From an instructional perspective, manuscript writing can be learned readily and, as any teacher is quick to point out, if all things are equal, ease of acquisition is a major consideration in choosing among different instructional methods.

Manuscript writing is readily acquired because it is consistent with the perceptual and motor development of primary grade children. The vertical and horizontal lines and circles of manuscript letters are easily perceived by young children and can be made without difficulty. Manuscript letters are spaced apart rather than being connected, and there are only six basic strokes to learn. This requires much less sustained muscular control.

LEGIBILITY

It is agreed that manuscript is more legible than cursive. Did you ever wonder why highway signs are in manuscript-type letters rather than cursive or italic? Imagine driving at 55 miles per hour on a crowded, unfamiliar highway. You are nearing a complex intersection of exits and approach ramps, and you think this is where you are to turn. Would you prefer the signs to be in a manuscript form, in cursive, or in italic?

Legibility is important because recognizing symbols is a prerequisite to understanding and using them. Anyone who has tried to master a foreign language knows that comprehension increases as rate of speech decreases. The same rule applies to visual language: more readable letters are learned at a faster rate and understood more completely.

As you would guess, legibility is a more important consideration for children than for adults. The adult who is well acquainted with the written form of language can "fill in" and is at no great disadvantage when a poorly written passage is encountered. Primary age children, however, are less acquainted with written language, so it is essential that their first writing experience be based on as legible a script as possible. After all, they are expected to read their own writing.

If cursive or italic is the initial style of writing a child learns, then it is probable that more time will be required and greater frustration will be encountered than if manuscript were taught. Under these conditions, even the most patient and capable children will find learning to write a chore. Moreover, children must learn two alphabets: the slanting, joined style that is written and the vertical, unjoined style that appears in the books they read.

A SKILL FRAMEWORK

The child who has only a brief introduction to manuscript will experience the same frustration. When manuscript is introduced in the first grade and cursive in the early part of second grade, the child never really masters manuscript. Hence, cursive writing, rather than being based on a solid foundation, is built on an unstable and incomplete substructure.

An analogy can be drawn between spoken and written language. The child who has spent the first four or five years of life in a linguistically rich environment will have good expressive and receptive auditory language skills. Upon this skill framework, the visual language skills (reading and writing) can be built. Compare this situation with manuscript and cursive writing. The child who spends sufficient time on manuscript to reach a level of competence will have an easier time with cursive writing. In learning to use both visual and auditory language, what comes after is built on what came before.

Since manuscript writing approximates the printed words in the readers to which children are first exposed, it is natural to expect that the early use of manuscript writing will promote the development of related skills such as reading.

And, indeed, manuscript has been found to be superior to cursive in its influence on beginning reading, spelling, and composition in the early grades. Children who use manuscript are more accomplished and expressive writers because they concentrate less on the mechanics involved in writing.

CLASSROOM ORGANIZATION

Learning Centers

Learning centers, when properly used in the classroom, can serve as an excellent means of motivation, reinforcement, expanding concepts, enrichment, meeting individual needs, integrating the language arts, and connecting handwriting with other areas of the curriculum. The information provided here gives suggestions to help you accomplish these objectives.

The learning center is an area of the room containing a variety of activities that reinforce or enrich skills and concepts already taught. It should not be a place where students are expected to acquire new formal skills, but should provide meaningful practice in those skills already introduced. The center is a means of organizing independent activities. Once the activities and procedures are understood, operation of the center is directed by the students. While the writing center may contain materials about handwriting or the writing process, the basis for other centers may be a subject or topic such as sports, weather, or an academic area.

The placement of a center is determined by such factors as electrical outlets, traffic patterns, and available space. The location may also be influenced by the number of students using the center at one time and whether activities will be completed at the center.

These illustrations are of possible classroom arrangements for learning centers.

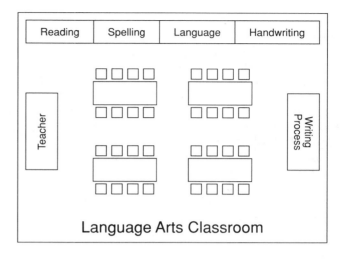

Language Arts Classroom

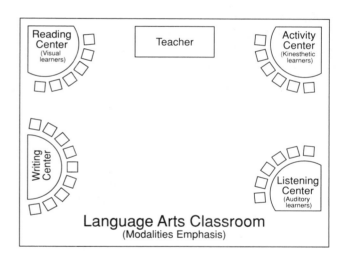

Language Arts Classroom
(Modalities Emphasis)

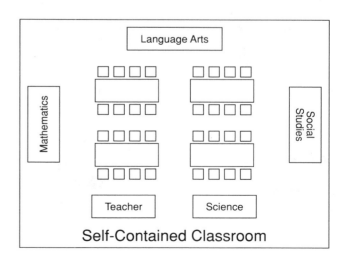

Self-Contained Classroom

Use of Chalkboard

Every classroom should be arranged to make maximum use of the chalkboard. Furniture should be placed in a manner that does not obstruct the chalkboard. Students should be able to see the chalkboard easily where they are seated without having to move their desks or adjust their sitting posture.

A chalkboard that is used correctly can be a most effective tool for handwriting instruction. It can be used to demonstrate letters large enough for students to see easily. Students can use gross motor skills as they write large letters on the chalkboard and then can analyze and discuss the basic strokes within the letters.

The writing lines, which consist of a headline, a midline, and a baseline, play a major role during the initial instruction of letterforms. The writing lines on the chalkboard should relate in color and style to those shown in the textbook and on the practice paper used. The writing lines must be introduced just as a new letter would be introduced. Each line, its name, and its color should be discussed by the teacher and students before any letters are introduced. Many students may never have seen the writing lines before and will be confused when the words **headline**, **midline**, and **baseline** are mentioned. As you point to each line on the chalkboard, ask the following questions: "Why do we call this line the headline (midline, baseline)? What color is the headline (midline, baseline)? On what line do the letters rest?" Writing lines are used to identify starting and stopping points of strokes within letters, and they must be mentioned when discussing a letter or when saying the stroke description of a letter. Writing lines on the chalkboard are crucial for effective handwriting instruction; therefore, if chalkboard space is available permanent writing lines should be considered. If chalkboard space is limited, a chalkboard line scriber should be used. The lines can be used when needed and then erased.

The writing spaces must be wide enough so the letters or words can be read easily by all students in the classroom. Study the examples below, which show the size of the writing spaces recommended for different levels.

Kindergarten

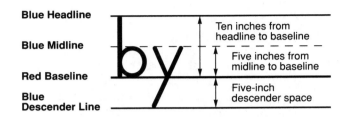

Blue Headline
Blue Midline
Red Baseline
Blue Descender Line

Ten inches from headline to baseline
Five inches from midline to baseline
Five-inch descender space

Grades One Through Four

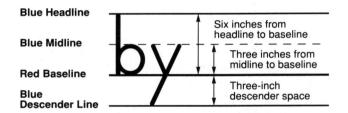

Blue Headline
Blue Midline
Red Baseline
Blue Descender Line

Six inches from headline to baseline
Three inches from midline to baseline
Three-inch descender space

Grades Five and Six

Headline
Five inches from headline to baseline
Baseline

by hot

You may wish to add thin lines to indicate proportion

Baseline

Permanent Writing Lines

One of the first things to consider when putting permanent writing lines on the chalkboard is the color of the chalkboard. If the chalkboard is black or a dark green or brown, a white opaque marker can be used to draw the lines.* You can then go over each line with a permanent marker in the proper color. (Or you could apply the lines with spray paint or chalk and fixative, two techniques that are described later.)

The placement of the writing lines on the chalkboard is also very important. You may wish to have two sets of permanent writing lines, one on which you can demonstrate letters and one on which the students can practice the letters. The baseline should be slightly lower than shoulder height. (Because the heights of the students will vary, an approximate placement must be established by the teacher.)

First, determine the size of the writing spaces needed on the chalkboard. Then establish the placement of the lines by making a rough chalk sketch of the lines. Look at the lines you have sketched and ask yourself if they are the proper height and whether the students will be able to clearly see what is written.

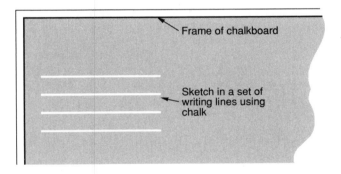

Frame of chalkboard

Sketch in a set of writing lines using chalk

Using a ruler, measure the distance from the top of the chalkboard to the headline of the lines you sketched. Place a blue dot where the headline is sketched on the chalkboard, and mark the ruler to indicate the distance from the edge of the chalkboard to the headline.

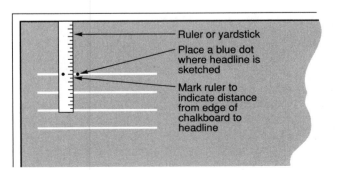

Ruler or yardstick

Place a blue dot where headline is sketched

Mark ruler to indicate distance from edge of chalkboard to headline

Using the same measurement, make several blue dots across the board about ten inches apart.

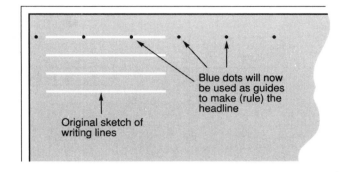

Blue dots will now be used as guides to make (rule) the headline

Original sketch of writing lines

Using a blue permanent marker and a straightedge, connect the blue dots. This will be the headline.

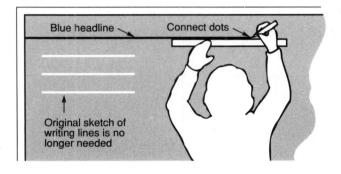

Blue headline

Connect dots

Original sketch of writing lines is no longer needed

Measure three inches down from the blue headline that you have just completed. Add several blue dots across the board. Using a blue marker, connect the dots with a broken line. This will be the midline.

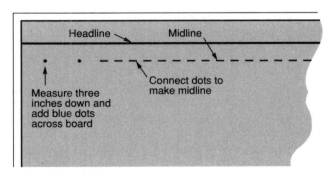

Headline

Midline

Connect dots to make midline

Measure three inches down and add blue dots across board

Continue by measuring three inches down from the midline that you just made. Add several **red** dots across the board. Using a red permanent marker, connect the dots. This will be the red baseline.

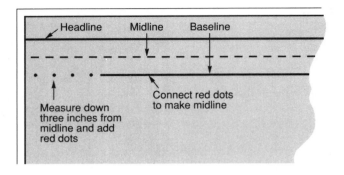

Measure three inches down from the baseline. Add several blue dots across the board. Using a blue permanent marker, connect the dots to create a descender space. You now have a complete set of permanent writing lines.

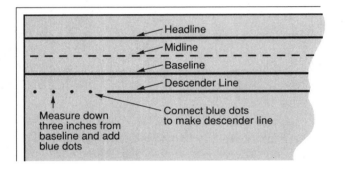

Permanent writing lines can also be put on the chalkboard using spray paint.* Following the measurements given above, use masking tape and newspaper to cover all areas of the chalkboard except those where the writing lines will appear. Be sure to cover the red baseline when you are spraying the blue headline, midline, and descender line. Be sure to spray the writing lines at a time when the classroom can be well ventilated. Read the caution label on the spray can carefully. Secure permission from your principal before you spray paint the writing lines on the chalkboard.

Another technique for making permanent writing lines is to draw the lines on the chalkboard using colored chalk and then spray the colored lines lightly with a fixative.* Let it dry and then spray it again. The chalk should not erase after being fixed.

*Because chalkboard surfaces vary, it is recommended that you try the permanent marker, paint, or chalk and fixative on a small section of the chalkboard first.

TEACHING HANDWRITING THROUGH MODALITY STRENGTHS

Teachers agree that the mode through which information is presented influences the efficiency with which children acquire and retain the information. Some children learn best when information is presented through a single modality or when one modality is dominant. For the child with a dominant modality, learning is most enjoyable and efficient when a lesson or skill is taught through the strongest sensory modality. Other children learn well whether the material is presented auditory, visual, or kinesthetic modes. These children are said to have a mixed modality strength.

A Modality-based Handwriting Curriculum

Handwriting is essentially a kinesthetic task, so many teachers believe that there is no way to teach it effectively through the other modalities. Quite the opposite is true. The following list of objectives can serve as the foundation of a handwriting curriculum that relies on each of the three educationally relevant modalities.

1. Visual (with model)
   a. Given letter models, writes lowercase manuscript letters
   b. Given letter models, writes uppercase manuscript letters
   c. Given numeral models, writes numerals *1-30*
   d. Given models, writes number words *one-ten*
   e. Given letter models, writes without reversing letters that are frequently reversed: *b-d, p-g-q*
   f. Given word models, writes without reversing words that are frequently reversed: *on-no, was-saw*
   g. Given letter models, writes lowercase letters grouped by similarity of strokes
   h. Given letter models, writes uppercase letters grouped by similarity of strokes
   i. Given models, writes punctuation marks: period, comma, question mark, exclamation mark, quotation marks

2. Auditory (with oral directions)
   a. Told letter names, writes lowercase manuscript letters
   b. Told letter names, writes uppercase manuscript letters
   c. Given letter sound, writes letter
   d. Told letter names, says letter strokes
   e. Told numeral names, writes numerals *1-30*
   f. Told numeral names, writes number words *one-ten*
   g. Given oral directions, writes lowercase letters grouped by similarity of strokes
   h. Given oral directions, writes uppercase letters grouped by similarity of strokes
   i. Told names of punctuation marks, writes: period, comma, question mark, exclamation mark, quotation marks
   j. Told letter names, writes without reversing letters that are frequently reversed: *b-d, p-g-q*
   k. Told words, writes without reversing words that are frequently reversed: *on-no, was-saw*

3. Kinesthetic (with movement)
   a. Given example, traces or forms in air lowercase letters grouped by similarity of strokes
   b. Given example, traces or forms in air uppercase letters grouped by similarity of strokes
   c. Given example, traces numerals on paper and forms them in air

CAUTIONS TO THE TEACHER
Kinesthetic Learner

The kinesthetic learner is potentially the best handwriter in the class. Most often, however, the child with a dominant kinesthetic modality excels neither in handwriting nor in other subject areas. There are several reasons for this failure to excel.

1. Kinesthetic learners are reinforced differently from other learners. Auditory and visual learners find that their good academic performances, in handwriting or other areas, are praised or rewarded. Kinesthetic learners are reinforced for sitting still or simply staying out of trouble.
2. Kinesthetic learners are not expected to perform well. They have acquired reputations as poor learners and are not held to the same standards as other students are. Not surprisingly, kinesthetic learners "live down" to teacher expectations.
3. Kinesthetic learners are expected to progress to small writing at the same time as visual and auditory learners. At the chalkboard, or using blank paper or primary ruled paper, the kinesthetic learner does well. If this child is forced at too early a stage to change to adult size writing, or from manuscript to cursive, frustration and failure may result. Auditory learners like loud and clear sounds; visual learners like bright, bold displays; and kinesthetic learners like large-muscle activity. Taking away this large-muscle activity at too early a stage is the equivalent of mumbling for the auditory learner.

Auditory Learner

The list of objectives presented previously in this article can serve as the basis by which handwriting, a kinesthetic-visual task, can be taught efficiently to the auditory learner. There are some cautions, however, that can make this task much easier.
1. Visual models, the mainstay of handwriting education, do not work well with auditory learners when they are presented alone. These students do not pay close attention to visual cues and, as a consequence, fail to note the salient characteristics of each letter. Be sure to accompany written models with descriptions of the strokes involved. For example:

    The letter is lowercase **h**. Begin at the headline, pull down straight to the baseline; push up, curve forward and up to the midline, curve down, and pull down straight to the baseline.

2. Be consistent in the language you use to describe letters, strokes, shape, and so on. Nothing is more frustrating to the person who depends on auditory cues than having those cues change pointlessly.

Visual Learner

Children with a visual modality strength are often neat writers simply because they attend closely to their product. There is no guarantee, however, that a visual child will be a good writer. If you keep the following points in mind, you can increase the probability that a child whose strongest modality is visual will reach his or her potential in handwriting.
1. Be sure that the model you use is appropriate. The visual child is quick to notice subtle differences in a visual display. If writing is to serve as a model for the visual child, be sure it is done correctly.
2. A large model displayed in the front of the room is a good means by which to point out the characteristics of a correctly formed letter. Even better, however, is a model that the visual child can use at his or her desk. A near model can be referred to quickly and can be inspected more closely.
3. Be consistent in the models that you use. Letter shapes vary somewhat among handwriting programs. If you are not visual, you might not notice the difference, but your visual students will. Inconsistent models will result in inconsistent performance on the part of visual learners.

INITIAL INSTRUCTION AND THE POINT OF INTERVENTION

Every classroom consists of children with varied modality strengths. Therefore, initial handwriting instruction should occur in a way that involves all the modalities. Of course, you will be inclined to rely most heavily on those methods that are consistent with your own modality strength. Keep in mind, however, that not all the students in the class share your modality strength. Teach in the manner in which you are most comfortable, provide relevant cues for learners with modality strengths different from your own, and be quick to recognize the child who is not grasping the content of the lesson.

The time at which you recognize that one or more students have failed to grasp a lesson is called the *point of intervention*. We strongly suggest that at this time you rely on the child's modality strength. You may wish to use self-instructional materials, individualized instruction, or grouping of children with similar modality strengths. Whatever course you pursue, be sure that it is consistent with the child's modality strength.

OBSERVABLE CHARACTERISTICS
INDICATIVE OF MODALITY STRENGTH

	Visual	Auditory	Kinesthetic
Learning Style	Learns by seeing, watching demonstrations	Learns through verbal instructions from others or self	Learns by doing, direct involvement
Reading	Likes description; sometimes stops reading to stare into space and imagine scene; intense concentration	Enjoys dialogue, avoids lengthy description, unaware of illustrations; moves lips or subvocalizes	Prefers stories where action occurs early; fidgets when reading; handles books; not an avid reader
Spelling	Recognizes words by sight; relies on configuration of words	Uses a phonics approach; has auditory word attack skills	Often is a poor speller; writes words to determine whether they "feel" right
Handwriting	Tends to be good, particularly in early years; spacing and size are good; appearance is important	Has more difficulty learning in initial stages; tends to write lightly; says strokes when writing	Good initially, deteriorates when space becomes smaller; pushes harder on writing instrument
Memory	Remembers faces, forgets names; writes things down; takes notes	Remembers names, forgets faces; remembers by auditory repetition	Remembers best what was done, not what was seen or talked about
Imagery	Vivid imagination; thinks in pictures, visualizes in detail	Subvocalizes, thinks in sounds; details less important	Imagery not important; images that do occur are accompanied by movement
Distractibility	Generally unaware of sounds; distracted by visual disorder or movement	Easily distracted by sounds	Not attentive to visual, auditory presentation, so seems distractible
Problem Solving	Deliberate; plans in advance; organizes thoughts by writing them; lists problems	Talks problems out, tries solutions orally, subvocally; talks self through problem	Attacks problems physically; impulsive; often selects solution involving greatest activity
Response to Periods of Inactivity	Stares; doodles; finds something to watch	Hums; talks to self or to others	Fidgets; finds reasons to move; holds up hand
Response to New Situations	Looks around; examines structure	Talks about situation, pros and cons, what to do	Tries things out; touches, feels, manipulates
Emotionality	Somewhat repressed; stares when angry, cries easily, beams when happy; facial expression is a good index of emotion	Shouts with joy or anger; blows up verbally but soon calms down; expresses emotion through words and through changes in volume and pitch of voice	Jumps for joy; hugs, tugs, and pulls when happy; stamps, jumps, pounds, and stomps off when angry; general body tone is a good index of emotion

OBSERVABLE CHARACTERISTICS
INDICATIVE OF MODALITY STRENGTH

	Visual	Auditory	Kinesthetic
Communication	Quiet; does not talk at length; becomes impatient when extensive listening is required; may use words clumsily; describes without embellishment; uses words such as *see* and *look*	Enjoys listening but cannot wait to talk; descriptions are long but repetitive; likes hearing self and others talk; uses words such as *listen* and *hear*	Gestures when speaking; does not listen well; stands close when speaking or listening; quickly loses interest in detailed oral discourse; uses words such as *get* and *take*
General Appearance	Neat, meticulous, likes order; may choose not to vary appearance	Matching clothes not so important, can explain choices of clothes	Neat but soon becomes wrinkled through activity
Response to the Arts	Not particularly responsive to music; prefers the visual arts; tends not to voice appreciation of art of any kind, but can be deeply affected by visual displays; focuses on details and components rather than the work as a whole	Favors music; finds less appeal in visual art, but is readily able to discuss it; misses significant detail, but appreciates the work as a whole; is able to develop verbal association for all art forms; spends more time talking about pieces than looking at them	Responds to music by physical movement; prefers sculpture; touches statues and paintings; at exhibits stops only at those in which he or she can become physically involved; comments very little on any art form

INSTRUCTIONAL DESIGN

II

Pacing of Instruction

Handwriting instruction should be a part of your daily teaching schedule. This article helps you make the most effective use of the materials in the text and Teacher Resource Binder. Suggestions are also provided for evaluation.

Integrated Instruction

With the whole-language influence so prevalent today, *Handwriting: A Way to Self-Expression* provides teachers with a variety of literature to use in their classroom. There are also many opportunities for students to write creatively.

Teaching Steps

Three teaching steps are used throughout the series. This article explains these steps in depth.

Meeting Special Needs

The Left-hander Handwriting guidance for the left-handed student is the focus of this article. Simple activities to help determine hand dominance are provided, as are hints for establishing a beneficial writing environment for left-handed children.

Reversals in Reading and Writing This article discusses the effect of handwriting instruction on children with letter and word-reversal problems. Common reversal problems and their possible causes are examined, and techniques for prevention and correction are provided.

Evaluation

Pretest A valuable evaluation tool, the pretest provides a reference point that teachers can use to evaluate handwriting progress. (Note that this pretest can be given in addition to the pretest in the Student Edition.)

After students have completed the pretest, use it both to record your comments and suggestions and to plan your handwriting goals for each child. Save the test sheets as valuable indices during your periodic evaluation of the students' handwriting growth throughout the year. In addition, at the end of the school year they will be an important evaluation tool, in conjunction with the posttest.

Posttest The posttest is to be given at the end of the school year to evaluate the progress each student has made. Used in conjunction with the pretest results, it helps the teacher evaluate the students' progress in shape, size, slant, spacing, and smoothness. Using the Evaluation Scale to compare the posttest to the writing samples helps the teacher objectively determine the students' final handwriting scores.

Student Record This checklist of handwriting skills lets the teacher keep track of the skills that have been introduced and that have been satisfactorily mastered by each student.

Keys to Legibility *Handwriting: A Way to Self-Expression* is based on five keys to legibility. This article lists and gives examples of the five keys.

PACING OF INSTRUCTION

Handwriting: A Way to Self-Expression is a complete series for kindergarten through grade eight. Each text in the series, along with the Practice Masters in the Teacher Resource Binder, is designed for one full year of instruction in handwriting.

Each book is divided into sections that group the letters according to commonality: shape, size, beginning stroke, and ending stroke. The length of a section is determined by the number of letters presented in that particular section.

As a general rule, only one letter is introduced on a page in the student text. This page permits the practice of the letter an average of 30 times. At the end of each of these pages is an end-of-lesson evaluation. The student writes the letter three times and then compares this with his or her initial attempts to determine the amount of progress made. A Checkpoint or a Keys to Legibility Score Box may then be used to note needed improvement.

In some cases, one of these skill pages can be satisfactorily completed in one handwriting lesson of approximately 15 minutes. This may be the exception rather than the rule, however. A more realistic goal would be to devote two periods of 15 minutes each to a skill page, along with the Practice Master for reinforcement and application. A review page can generally be completed in one instructional period.

The end-of-lesson evaluation, located at the bottom of each skill page, is intended to provide students an opportunity to compare these three letters with their initial attempts on the page. It also permits the teacher to determine whether additional reinforcement or reteaching is needed.

INTEGRATED INSTRUCTION

Handwriting is a complex skill that needs to be developed in advance of its use. Before a child can write a friendly letter, he or she must know the acceptable alphabet forms that are needed to make up the words to be written, how to manage the paper and writing instrument, how to space properly, how to spell the words he or she wishes to use in the letter, and, to some degree, the parts of a friendly letter. To incorporate all this into one body of instruction would be overwhelming for the child and an impossible task for the teacher to accomplish. Writing a friendly letter brings together the elements that have been learned at different times, for different reasons, into a meaningful whole and provides a purpose for writing. Every opportunity to relate handwriting to reading, spelling, and other areas of the curriculum should be taken. The thematic organization of the series makes this kind of teaching easier.

Literature

Each section of the student text begins with a poem or example of another literary genre that sets the tone and theme for that particular section. These interactive features are driven by questions and answers found in the Teacher Edition.

Writing Process

You will find many opportunities for students to write creatively, using their own language. These situations may be a kind of springboard for sustained writing, using the recognized steps in the writing process. It is important to keep in mind that correct handwriting and spelling are not emphasized until the editing step, at which time attention is given to all elements of composition.

Steps in the Writing Process

Prewriting Prewriting strategies may consist of: brainstorming ideas; clustering, mapping, or webbing; outlining; interviewing; role-playing; questioning; categorizing; listing; and reading.

Writing (Drafting) Drafting involves organizing ideas, choosing words, composing sentences, and developing paragraphs.

Revising Revising consists of: conferencing, expanding, or deleting ideas; reorganizing ideas; improving sentence structure; and adding interest to beginning and ending.

Editing Proofreading and correcting errors in mechanics, usage, and form take place during the editing stage.

Publishing Publishing may take on any of the following forms: sharing orally, displaying on a bulletin board, placing in the classroom library, printing in a school or local newspaper, entering in a contest, or mailing to a friend or relative.

TEACHING STEPS

Focus (Develop Imagery)

One of the strengths of the Zaner-Bloser program is the method for developing imagery. Through discussion, demonstration, and direction, imagery is developed through a combination of visual, auditory, and kinesthetic experiences. Imagery is developed sequentially:

Focus (Visual, Auditory) The mental image is developed by guiding students in perceiving (seeing in the mind's eye) the shape of the letter. The teacher presents and names the letterform. The enlarged letter in the Model Box is to be used for this step. The arrows and numerals indicate the direction and sequence of strokes. Auditory learners will need to "talk through" (verbalize) the letter as the various parts are traced in the air. Students are then asked to help determine what strokes make up the letter and where each stroke begins and ends. Selected questions for discussion of each letter will appear on the skill pages.

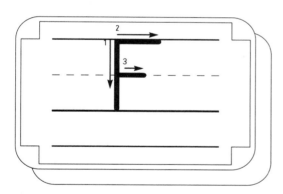

Model (Visual, Auditory) The second stage is developed through visual and auditory means. The teacher demonstrates the letter in a large size on the chalkboard on ruled lines as she or he says the stroke description of the letter ("Pull down straight, lift, slide right, lift, slide right"). This should be repeated two or three times.

Model (Kinesthetic) The third stage is developing the motor image or the image of the sequence and direction of the strokes. This is developed through tracing the letter models with the fingers and nonwriting end of the pencil. The letter model in the Model Box and the screened model are used for this step. The ability to transfer the image from the mind to the muscle (neuromuscular response) is reinforced by forming the letter in the air and on the desk before actually writing it.

Write and Evaluate (Determine Needs)

Write Students will write the letter or letter combination three times on paper without a model and/or write the first line of letters in the Student Edition.

Evaluate The paper is now folded on the line above the three letters and placed beneath the model in the textbook. Students compare their letters with the model and draw a line under the best letter and an X under the one that needs the most improvement. Teachers who do not have Zaner-Bloser paper may prefer that initial practice be done in the Student Edition. This makes self-evaluation more difficult, but the Peek Thru Overlay can be used in place of folded paper.

Apply (Direct Improvement)

Practice The teacher will quickly note children who have done well. They will proceed to practice the letter either on paper or in the spaces provided in the textbook. Meaningful application of the skill is essential. Practice that has no purpose and is without meaningful content is not effective.

Students who need reteaching should receive instruction according to their dominant sensory modality. (See instructions for teaching the visual, auditory, and kinesthetic learners.)

MEETING SPECIAL NEEDS

THE LEFT-HANDER

We live in a right-handed society. Our civilization has been built around a tradition that regards the right hand as preferable to the left. Hand tools, machines, even doors were designed on the basis of this attitude. However, several years ago, Dr. Frank Freeman observed:

"The number of left-handed children seems to have increased in recent years. This may be due to relaxed home and school discipline as well as the recommendations of medical authorities that children who show early preference for the left hand should not be changed. Whatever the reason, these children are entitled to just as much guidance and help in the development of the skill of handwriting as the right-hander receives."*

Recent studies indicate that the number of left-handers is still on the increase. Estimates range as high as ten to 15 percent of the population. Almost assuredly, the elementary teacher will be teaching handwriting not only to right-handed children but will also have the responsibility of instructing the left-handers.

Determining Hand Dominance

How can one decide which hand the child should use in writing? Wrong choices at the readiness and early primary level could be detrimental to the child's writing and perhaps to the child's learning ability and personality. The choice, then, is an important one.

If the child is definitely left-handed, it is better to teach her or him to use that hand in writing. If, however, there is some doubt as to which is the dominant hand, there are several simple ways of determining which will be the hand to train.

A few guidelines should be observed in these procedures. Do not tell the child that she or he is being tested. Work with only one child at a time. Keep a record as to which hand is used for each specific situation. Let the child pick up the testing materials; do not hand them to the child. Keep a tally of the procedures. If the child indicates true ambidexterity, it is probably better to train the right hand.

Several procedures are listed below. There are many other simple play situations that the observant teacher will find helpful for determining hand dominance.

Hand puppet Place a hand puppet on the table. In a play situation, observe the child to see which hand she or he puts the puppet on.

Key and lock Padlock a cupboard in the classroom. Place the key on the desk. Ask the child to take the key and unlock the padlock and bring you an object from the cupboard. Observe the child as she or he unlocks the padlock and picks up the object.

Hammering nails Place a toy hammer and nails or pegs and pegboard on the table. Observe the child as she or he hammers several nails into place, or puts pegs into pegboard.

Screwing lids on jars Place several jars of various sizes with removable lids on the table. Place the lids in a separate pile. Ask the child to match the lids with the jars, put the lids on the jars, and close them.

Throwing a ball Place a rubber ball on the floor. Ask the child to pick up the ball and throw it to you.

Holding a spoon At lunchtime, or in a play situation where the child must use eating utensils, observe which hand is used.

Cutting with scissors Place a pair of scissors and a piece of colored construction paper on the table. Instruct the child to cut the paper into strips. Observe which hand is used to pick up the scissors and to cut the paper. Next, place paper of a different color on the table and have the child repeat the process. Did the child use the same hand or change hands? Repeat with a third color.

*Freeman, Frank N. *Reference Manual for Teachers, Grades One through Four*. Columbus, Ohio: Zaner-Bloser Company, 1959, p. 28.

Position for Writing

For manuscript writing, the left-handed child should tilt the top of the paper up and toward the right (about 35 to 45 degrees is recommended). For cursive writing, the top of the paper should be tilted up and toward the right. The strokes are pulled down toward the left elbow, whether manuscript or cursive is being written.

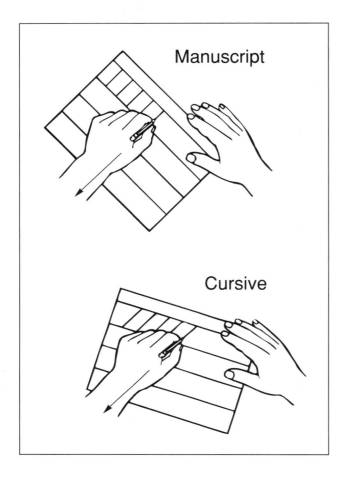

The writing instrument is held between the thumb and first two fingers, about an inch above its point. The first finger rests on the top of the pencil or pen. The end of the bent thumb is placed against the writing instrument to hold it high in the hand and near the large knuckle. The top of the instrument points in the direction of the upper arms and shoulders.

The writing should take place within the left half of the desk surface, i.e., to the left of the midline of the body. The paper should be shifted to the left as the writing progresses across the page.

Special Problems

The Hooked Position In an effort to see what she or he is writing, the left-handed child often adopts the hooked position. This is a problem that must be dealt with early in the child's development, since twisting of the hand or wrist can be detrimental to legibility and fluency. A valuable aid for this problem is the Zaner-Bloser Writing Frame, designed to assist the child in holding the writing instrument correctly.

Reversals The problem of reversals is common to the left-handed child. Most errors result from confusion between the lowercase manuscript **d** and **b** and **p** and **q**. Awareness of the problem and concentration on the formal teaching of left to right progression and forward and backward circles before introduction of the teaching of the manuscript letters **b**, **d**, **p**, and **q** result in fewer reversals of these letters.

Chalkboard Work

Chalkboard practice is important because it lends itself to full, free arm movement. The position at the board for left-handed writing is similar to that for writing with the right hand, except that the eraser is held in the right hand and the chalk in the left, and the left-hander stands to the right of where the writing takes place for both manuscript and cursive. This is not true of the right-hander. The right-hander stands in front of his or her manuscript writing, but stands to the left of cursive writing.

REVERSALS IN READING AND WRITING

The child who reverses letters and words presents a challenge for the teacher at all grade levels. Teaching handwriting offers a unique opportunity (1) to minimize the chance of reversals and (2) to correct reversals once they have occurred.

Handwriting depends primarily on large and small-muscle control and thereby allows the introduction of an effective teaching style other than the verbal and auditory styles that are so often depended upon in other language arts areas.

While the reversing of letters and words is a problem, a more complex aspect of the same problem is inversions. Reversals occur in letters or words with similar configurations but different left to right orientation:

b–d   on–no
g–q   saw–was

Inversions occur with letters that are similar but have a different top to bottom orientation:

n–u   p–d   h-y

Reversals and inversions may occur when the child is attempting new and unfamiliar letterforms or difficult words that have not been fully learned. Unfamiliarity is therefore one cause. Strain and fatigue are other causes. The teacher should avoid lengthy writing assignments, particularly at a time of the day when the child's energy level is low. This is especially true in initial handwriting instruction or for instructing the child who has already demonstrated reversal tendencies.

Immaturity is also one of the causes of reversals; for the child whose eyes are not sufficiently mature to perceive differences in letters or whose coordination is not developed enough for him or her to reproduce letters, occasional reversals are normal. Overconcern should not be evident at this point in the child's development, for if the child comes to associate failure with attempts at writing, he or she will have difficulty overcoming a reversal tendency.

Reversals are not necessarily a direct cause of poor reading, but obviously the child who cannot decide whether the word begins with **b** or **d** is unable to use word attack skills to figure it out. The teacher can diagnose this problem merely by observing the type of error that a child makes. It would be wise not to correct the child at the time he or she makes the error, but instead to note the difficulty and later deal with the child individually.

Preventive Techniques and Activities

Activities should be used that require the student to demonstrate a visual and motor response to directionality. Early activities might include placing an object, such as a stuffed animal, in the correct position when given a picture model (up, down, over, under, in, out, left, right, top, bottom). This activity is followed by placing cutout figures in the correct position using a picture model. At a still more advanced level, the child is asked to respond with a line or circle mark when given a model.

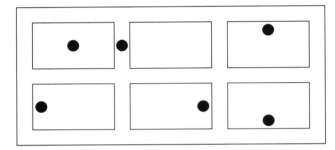

Since an early emphasis on left to right movement is important, teachers need to provide extensive activities using a left to right sweep of the teacher's hand as he or she reads from a book or the chalkboard. The children should be encouraged to move their hands along written material in a similar manner. Another activity to emphasize left to right progression is to have students name objects and move their fingers across the objects when presented with the pictured objects on a page. The teacher should give the directions: "Move your fingers across each line from left to right . . . ."

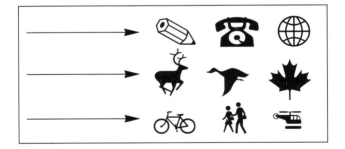

Figures placed on a felt board are also helpful. The child is asked to tell what the figures are and is asked to name them from left to right. The figures are removed and the child is to replace them in the same sequence.

As new letters or words are introduced, a tracing-sounding method may be used. This method seems to reduce the reversal problems for some children. The muscular response strengthens the orientation image. It may be beneficial for the child to verbalize the directions or stroke sequence used to form a letter.

Before the children learn to write individual letters, it is wise to have them master the basic strokes (i.e., left to right, top to bottom, backward circle, forward circle, slant right, slant left). Once the basic strokes are mastered, it is possible to teach the formation of the lowercase **d** as a backward circle and a top to bottom line and the lowercase **b** as a top to bottom line and a forward circle. Exaggerating the differences in these two letters may help the children avoid later reversals.

Having the writing model on the child's desk is one preventive technique. This eliminates the strain of looking up at the chalkboard. In chalkboard writing, the model should be placed directly in front of the child and above his or her most comfortable writing level.

Of course, one of the most important preventive measures is to be sure the child is ready for writing. Determine whether the child shows:

1. mastery of gross motor skills such as walking, running, jumping, hopping, etc.;
2. mastery of gross visual and auditory discrimination such as seeing obvious differences in objects large and small, in different positions, and of different colors; and in hearing differences in loud and soft sounds and high and low pitch;
3. mastery of visual-motor skills such as following a moving object with head and eyes, walking along a marked path, and following a line with one's fingers;
4. mastery of sufficient basic vocabulary to comprehend directions given orally;
5. eagerness to handle a writing instrument by wanting to draw or color.

EVALUATION

PRETEST

A valuable evaluation tool, the pretest provides a reference point that teachers can use to evaluate handwriting progress. Students should be made to understand that the pretest is just what the name implies—a test taken *before* any new material is introduced. Consequently, it is not a test to be studied for or one that will be graded; the only preparation is the student's commitment to doing his or her best.

After students have completed the pretest, use it both to record your comments and your suggestions and to plan your handwriting goals for each child. Save the test sheets, for they will be valuable indices during your periodic evaluation of the students' handwriting growth throughout the year. In addition, at the end of the school year the pretest, in conjunction with the posttest, will be an important evaluation tool.

POSTTEST

The posttest is to be given at the end of the school year to evaluate the progress each student has made. Used in conjunction with the pretest results, it helps the teacher evaluate the students' overall progress. Comparing the posttest to the writing samples on the Evaluation Scale helps the teacher objectively determine the students' final handwriting scores.

EVALUATION SCALE
(in binder pocket)

The Evaluation Scale contains samples of students' writing that range from excellent to poor, prepared by compiling and evaluating specimens of student work from across the United States. Each sample was carefully evaluated according to the keys to legibility. The Evaluation Scale, which can be a valuable tool in your classroom writing center, should be posted in a place where students can easily see it and use it for self-evaluation. The scale can also be used by teachers for evaluating students' handwriting papers.

PEEK THRU OVERLAYS
(in binder pocket)

The Peek Thru Overlays are used by the students as evaluation aids during self-evaluation lessons and by the teacher when evaluating student papers. The overlays are designed to correspond with the writing lines and letterforms in the students' books. Place the overlays over the written letters to check for correct letter formation and alignment. *Note:* It will be helpful to have several sets of these evaluation tools at the writing center, as well as several sets to circulate among the students during handwriting lessons.

ALPHABET WALL CHART
(in binder pocket)

The Alphabet Wall Chart should be posted at the students' eye level in the writing center where students can easily see and use it. The chart is especially helpful to those students who need a reference to remember the formation of difficult letters. The letters on the chart are grouped by stroke similarities to promote learning through recognition of the relationships that exist between the various letterforms.

Pretest — Manuscript

Write the sentences. Use your best handwriting.

My name stands for me. I want to write it well.

Keys to Legibility Score Box

Check:	Satisfactory	Needs to Improve
size	□	□
shape	□	□
slant (vertical quality)	□	□
spacing	□	□
smoothness	□	□

Posttest — Manuscript

Write the sentences. Use your best handwriting.

My name stands for me. I want to write it well.

Keys to Legibility Score Box

Check:	Satisfactory	Needs to Improve
size	☐	☐
shape	☐	☐
slant (vertical quality)	☐	☐
spacing	☐	☐
smoothness	☐	☐

B30

Student Record of Handwriting Skills
Grade 1

Student's Name _____

	Needs Improvement	Mastery of Skill
Writes top to bottom stroke.	☐	☐
Positions paper properly.	☐	☐
Writes left to right stroke.	☐	☐
Holds pencil properly.	☐	☐
Writes backward circle.	☐	☐
Writes the forward circle.	☐	☐
Writes slant right stroke.	☐	☐
Writes slant left stroke.	☐	☐
Writes the letter l.	☐	☐
Writes the letter i.	☐	☐
Writes the letter t.	☐	☐
Writes the letter o.	☐	☐
Writes the period.	☐	☐
Writes the letter a.	☐	☐
Writes the letter d.	☐	☐
Writes the letter c.	☐	☐
Writes the letter e.	☐	☐
Writes the letter f.	☐	☐
Writes the letter g.	☐	☐
Writes the letter j.	☐	☐
Writes the letter q.	☐	☐
Writes the letter u.	☐	☐
Writes the letter s.	☐	☐
Writes the letter b.	☐	☐
Writes the question mark.	☐	☐
Writes the letter p.	☐	☐
Writes the letter r.	☐	☐
Writes the letter n.	☐	☐
Writes the exclamation mark.	☐	☐
Writes the letter m.	☐	☐
Writes the letter h.	☐	☐
Writes the letter v.	☐	☐
Writes the letter y.	☐	☐
Writes the letter w.	☐	☐
Writes the letter k.	☐	☐
Writes the letter x.	☐	☐
Writes the letter z.	☐	☐
Writes the numeral 1.	☐	☐

	Needs Improvement	Mastery of Skill
Writes the numeral 2.	☐	☐
Writes the numeral 3.	☐	☐
Writes the numeral 4.	☐	☐
Writes the numeral 5.	☐	☐
Writes the numeral 6.	☐	☐
Writes the numeral 7.	☐	☐
Writes the numeral 8.	☐	☐
Writes the numeral 9.	☐	☐
Writes the numeral 10.	☐	☐
Writes the letter L.	☐	☐
Writes the letter I.	☐	☐
Writes the quotation mark.	☐	☐
Writes the letter T.	☐	☐
Writes the letter E.	☐	☐
Writes the letter F.	☐	☐
Writes the letter H.	☐	☐
Writes the letter O.	☐	☐
Writes the letter Q.	☐	☐
Writes the comma.	☐	☐
Writes the letter C.	☐	☐
Writes the letter G.	☐	☐
Writes the apostrophe.	☐	☐
Writes the letter P.	☐	☐
Writes the letter R.	☐	☐
Writes the letter B.	☐	☐
Writes the letter D.	☐	☐
Writes the letter U.	☐	☐
Writes the letter S.	☐	☐
Writes the letter J.	☐	☐
Writes the letter A.	☐	☐
Writes the letter N.	☐	☐
Writes the letter M.	☐	☐
Writes the letter V.	☐	☐
Writes the letter W.	☐	☐
Writes the letter Y.	☐	☐
Writes the letter K.	☐	☐
Writes the letter X.	☐	☐
Writes the letter Z.	☐	☐

KEYS TO LEGIBILITY FOR MANUSCRIPT HANDWRITING

SHAPE (Letter Formation) The six basic strokes that determine the correctness of shape of all manuscript letters are:

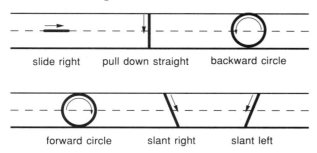

SIZE (Height of Letters) The letters should rest on the baseline, and they must take up the right amount of space above the baseline. There are three heights of letters:

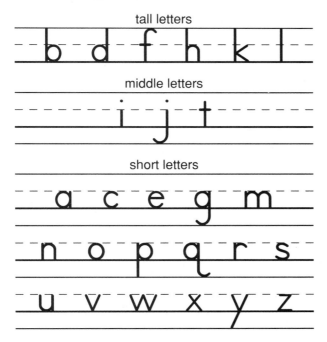

SPACING (Distance between letters, words, and sentences) Readability is greatly improved when proper spacing is used.

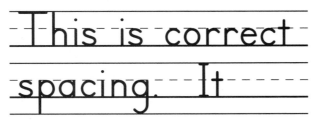

SLANT (Vertical Quality) The vertical quality is obtained by

- positioning the paper properly,
- pulling the downstrokes in the proper direction, and
- shifting the paper as the writing line progresses.

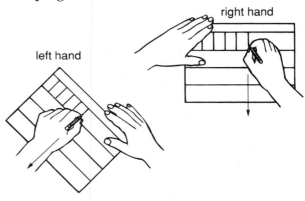

SMOOTHNESS (Line Quality) Line quality is affected by the kind of writing instrument used, the way the writing instrument is held, the amount of finger movement, and how much pressure is applied to the writing instrument.

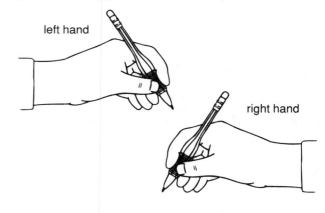

INSTRUCTIONAL SUPPORT

III

Stroke Descriptions—English

Once students are able to recognize letters, these oral stroke descriptions can be used in conjunction with the letter models and the visual demonstrations of the strokes to help students learn the proper progression of the steps necessary to form uppercase letters, lowercase letters, and numerals 1-10.

Since students learn in three different modalities (visual, auditory, and kinesthetic), a three-pronged approach to these stroke descriptions provides maximum understanding and information retention by all students:

- Visual — Some students need only to see the handwriting strokes demonstrated to learn to reproduce them successfully.
- Auditory — Some students need to hear each letter described as well as to see the strokes demonstrated.
- Kinesthetic — Some students need both to see the letters demonstrated and to hear them described, but they retain information best after physically practicing the motions of the various strokes.

Stroke Descriptions—Spanish

The same stroke descriptions provided in English are also given in Spanish. Students for whom English is a second language will find these descriptions helpful.

Supportive Materials

The authors of *Handwriting: A Way to Self-Expression* have made every attempt possible to give you, the teacher, all the support you need for an effective instructional program in handwriting. Many supportive materials are found in the binder pockets: transparencies, charts, worksheets, and Peek Thru Overlays. A description of the use and purpose of each of these items is given on the following pages. You will find references to these materials in the Teacher Edition.

Evaluation Certificates

Certificates of recognition are important in building pride and self-esteem. Certificates of Progress should be awarded to those students who show notable handwriting progress and Certificates of Excellence to those who progress to the top levels of handwriting ability.

Certificates may be decorated with stickers or enhanced by the addition of color. Rolled and tied with appropriate ribbons, they may be presented in special award ceremonies. They may also be proudly displayed near the writing center.

Manuscript Stroke Descriptions— English

Alphabet

 Touch the headline and **slant left** to the baseline. **Lift.** Touch the headline and **slant right** to the baseline. **Lift.** Touch the first stroke below the midline and **slide right.**

 Touch halfway between the midline and baseline and **circle back** (left) all the way around. **Lift.** Touch the midline and **pull down straight** to the baseline.

or

Touch halfway between the midline and baseline and **circle back** (left) all the way around. **Push up straight** to the midline. **Pull down straight** to the baseline.

 Touch the headline and **pull down straight** to the baseline. **Lift.** Touch the headline and **slide right; curve forward** to the midline; **slide left. Stop. Slide right; curve forward** to the baseline; **slide left.**

 Touch the headline and **pull down straight** to the baseline. **Lift.** Touch halfway between the midline and baseline and **circle forward** (right) all the way around.

or

Touch the headline and **pull down straight** to the baseline. **Push up** to halfway between the midline and baseline and **circle forward** (right) all the way around.

 Touch below the headline and **circle back** (left), ending above the baseline.

 Touch below the midline and **circle back** (left), ending above the baseline.

 Touch the headline and **pull down straight** to the baseline. **Lift.** Touch the headline and **slide right; curve forward** to the baseline; **slide left.**

 Touch halfway between the midline and baseline and **circle back** (left) all the way around. **Lift.** Touch the headline and **pull down straight** to the baseline.

or

Touch halfway between the midline and baseline and **circle back** (left) all the way around. **Push up straight** to the headline. **Pull down straight** to the baseline.

 Touch the headline and **pull down straight** to the baseline. **Stop. Slide right. Lift.** Touch the headline and **slide right. Lift.** Touch the midline and **slide right.** Stop short.

 Touch halfway between the midline and baseline and **slide right; circle back** (left), ending above the baseline.

or

Touch halfway between the midline and baseline and **circle back** (left), ending above the baseline. **Lift.** Touch halfway and **slide right.**

 Touch the headline and **pull down straight** to the baseline. **Lift.** Touch the headline and **slide right. Lift.** Touch the midline and **slide right.** Stop short.

 Touch below the headline and **curve back** (left); **pull down straight** to the baseline. **Lift.** Touch the midline and **slide right.**

 Touch below the headline and **circle back** (left), ending at the midline. **Slide left.**

Touch halfway between the midline and baseline and **circle back** (left) all the way around. **Lift.** Touch the midline and **pull down straight** through the baseline; **curve back** (left), touching the next guideline.

or

Touch halfway between the midline and baseline and **circle back** (left) all the way around. **Push up straight** to the midline. **Pull down straight** through the baseline; **curve back** (left), touching the next guideline.

Touch the headline and **pull down straight** to the baseline. **Lift.** Move to the right and touch the headline; **pull down straight** to the baseline. **Lift.** Move to the left and touch the midline; **slide right.**

Touch the headline and **pull down straight** to the baseline. **Stop. Push up** (retrace) and **curve forward** (right); **pull down straight** to the baseline.

Touch the headline and **slide right. Lift.** Touch the first stroke at the halfway point and **pull down straight** to the baseline. **Lift.** Touch the baseline and **slide right.**

Touch the midline and **pull down straight** to the baseline. **Lift. Dot** halfway between the headline and midline.

Touch the headline and **pull down straight; curve back** (left).

Touch the midline and **pull down straight** through the baseline; **curve back** (left), touching the next guideline. **Lift. Dot** halfway between the headline and midline.

Touch the headline and **pull down straight** to the baseline. **Lift.** Move to the right and touch the headline; **slant left** to the midline. **Stop. Slant right** to the baseline.

Touch the headline and **pull down straight** to the baseline. **Lift.** Move to the right and touch the midline; **slant left,** touching the stroke halfway between the midline and baseline. **Stop. Slant right** to the baseline.

Touch the headline and **pull down straight** to the baseline. **Stop. Slide right.**

Touch the headline and **pull down straight** to the baseline.

Touch the headline and **pull down straight** to the baseline. **Lift.** Touch the headline and **slant right** to the baseline. **Lift.** Move to the right and touch the headline; **slant left** to the baseline. **Lift.** Touch the headline and **pull down straight** to the baseline.

or

Touch the headline and **pull down straight** to the baseline. **Lift.** Touch the headline and **slant right** to the baseline. **Slant up** (right) to the headline. **Pull down straight** to the baseline.

Touch the midline and **pull down straight** to the baseline. **Stop. Push up** (retrace) and **curve forward** (right); **pull down straight** to the baseline. **Stop. Push up** (retrace) and **curve forward** (right); **pull down straight** to the baseline.

Touch the headline and **pull down straight** to the baseline. **Lift.** Touch the headline and **slant right** to the baseline. **Lift.** Touch the headline and **pull down straight** to the baseline.

or

Touch the headline and **pull down straight** to the baseline. **Lift.** Touch the headline and **slant right** to the baseline. **Push up straight** to the headline.

Touch the midline and **pull down straight** to the baseline. **Stop. Push up** (retrace) and **curve forward** (right); **pull down straight** to the baseline.

Touch the midline and **circle back** (left) all the way around.

Touch halfway between the midline and baseline and **circle back** (left) all the way around.

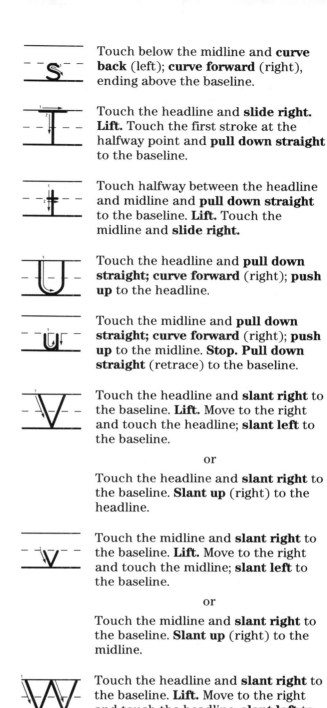

Touch the headline and **pull down straight** to the baseline. **Lift.** Touch the headline and **slide right; curve forward** (right) to the midline; **slide left.**

Touch the midline and **pull down straight** through the baseline to the next guideline. **Lift.** Touch halfway between the midline and baseline and **circle forward** (right) all the way around.

or

Touch the midline and **pull down straight** through the baseline to the next guideline. **Push up** to halfway between the baseline and midline and **circle forward** (right) all the way around.

Touch the midline and **circle back** (left) all the way around. **Lift.** Make a short **slant right** stroke through the circle at the lower right, ending on the baseline.

Touch halfway between the midline and baseline and **circle back** (left) all the way around. **Lift.** Touch the midline and **pull down straight** through the baseline; **curve forward** (right), touching the next guideline.

or

Touch halfway between the midline and baseline and **circle back** (left) all the way around. **Push up straight** to the midline. **Pull down straight** through the baseline; **curve forward** (right), touching the next guideline.

Touch the headline and **pull down straight** to the baseline. **Lift.** Touch the headline and **slide right; curve forward** (right) to the midline; **slide left. Lift.** Touch the midline and **slant right** to the baseline.

Touch the midline and **pull down straight** to the baseline. **Stop. Push up** (retrace) and **curve forward** (right), ending below the midline.

Touch below the headline and **curve back** (left); **curve forward** (right), ending above the baseline.

Touch below the midline and **curve back** (left); **curve forward** (right), ending above the baseline.

Touch the headline and **slide right. Lift.** Touch the first stroke at the halfway point and **pull down straight** to the baseline.

Touch halfway between the headline and midline and **pull down straight** to the baseline. **Lift.** Touch the midline and **slide right.**

Touch the headline and **pull down straight; curve forward** (right); **push up** to the headline.

Touch the midline and **pull down straight; curve forward** (right); **push up** to the midline. **Stop. Pull down straight** (retrace) to the baseline.

Touch the headline and **slant right** to the baseline. **Lift.** Move to the right and touch the headline; **slant left** to the baseline.

or

Touch the headline and **slant right** to the baseline. **Slant up** (right) to the headline.

Touch the midline and **slant right** to the baseline. **Lift.** Move to the right and touch the midline; **slant left** to the baseline.

or

Touch the midline and **slant right** to the baseline. **Slant up** (right) to the midline.

Touch the headline and **slant right** to the baseline. **Lift.** Move to the right and touch the headline; **slant left** to the baseline. **Lift.** Touch the headline and **slant right** to the baseline. **Lift.** Move to the right and touch the headline; **slant left** to the baseline.

or

Touch the headline and **slant right** to the baseline. **Slant up** (right) to the headline. **Slant right** to the baseline. **Slant up** (right) to the headline.

Touch the midline and **slant right** to the baseline. **Lift.** Move to the right and touch the midline; **slant left** to the baseline. **Lift.** Touch the midline and **slant right** to the baseline. **Lift.** Move to the right and touch the midline; **slant left** to the baseline.

or

Touch the midline and **slant right** to the baseline. **Slant up** (right) to the midline. **Slant right** to the baseline. **Slant up** (right) to the midline.

 Touch the headline and **slant right** to the baseline. **Lift.** Move to the right and touch the headline; **slant left** to the baseline.

 Touch the midline and **slant right** to the baseline. **Lift.** Move to the right and touch the midline; **slant left** to the baseline.

 Touch the headline and **slant right** to the midline. **Lift.** Move to the right and touch the headline; **slant left** to the midline. **Stop. Pull down straight** to the baseline.

 Touch the midline and **slant right** to the baseline. **Lift.** Move to the right and touch the midline; **slant left** through the baseline to the next guideline.

 Touch the headline and **slide right. Stop. Slant left** to the baseline. **Stop. Slide right.**

 Touch the midline and **slide right. Stop. Slant left** to the baseline. **Stop. Slide right.**

Numerals

 Touch the headline and **pull down straight** to the baseline.

 Touch below the headline and **curve forward** (right), touching the headline; **slant left** to the baseline. **Stop. Slide right.**

 Touch below the headline and **curve forward** (right) to the midline; **curve forward** (right), ending above the baseline.

 Touch the headline and **pull down straight** to the midline. **Stop. Slide right. Lift.** Touch the headline and **pull down straight** to the baseline, crossing the slide stroke.

 Touch the headline and **pull down straight** to the midline. **Stop. Circle forward** (right), ending above the baseline. **Lift.** Touch the headline and **slide right.**

 Touch the headline and **curve down** to the baseline; **curve up** to the midline and **around** to close the circle.

 Touch the headline and **slide right. Stop. Slant left** to the baseline.

 Touch below the headline and **curve back** (left); **curve forward** (right) touching the baseline; **slant up,** crossing the curve stroke and touching the beginning stroke. End at the headline.

Touch halfway between the headline and midline and **circle back** (left) all the way around. **Pull down straight** to the baseline.

 Touch the headline and **pull down straight** to the baseline. **Lift.** Touch the headline and **curve down** to the baseline; **curve up** to the headline.

Descripciónes de los trazos de la letra manuscrita

Abecedario

 Toque la línea superior y **haga un trazo inclinado hacia la izquierda** hasta la línea base. **Levante.** Toque la línea superior y **haga un trazo inclinado hacia la derecha** hasta la línea base. **Levante.** Toque el primer trazo debajo de la línea media y **siga el trazo hacia la derecha.**

 Toque en la mitad entre la línea media y la línea base y **trace un círculo completo hacia atrás** (hacia la izquierda). **Levante.** Toque la línea media y **haga un trazo recto hacia abajo** hasta la línea base.

o

Toque en la mitad entre la línea media y la línea base y **haga un círculo completo hacia atrás** (hacia la izquierda). **Trace una línea recta hacia arriba** hasta la línea media. **Trace una línea recta hacia abajo** hasta la línea base.

 Toque la línea superior y **haga un trazo recto hacia abajo** hasta la línea base. **Levante.** Toque la línea superior y **siga el trazo hacia la derecha; haga una curva hacia adelante** hasta la línea media; **siga el trazo hacia la izquierda. Pare. Siga el trazo hacia la derecha; haga una curva hacia adelante** hasta la línea base; **siga el trazo hacia la izquierda.**

 Toque la línea superior y **trace una línea recta hacia abajo** hasta la línea base. **Levante.** Toque en la mitad entre la línea media y la línea base y **haga un círculo completo hacia adelante** (hacia la derecha).

o

Toque en la línea superior y **trace una línea recta hacia abajo** hasta la línea base. **Trace una línea recta hacia arriba** hasta la mitad entre la línea media y la línea base y **haga un círculo completo hacia adelante** (hacia la derecha).

 Toque debajo de la línea superior e **inicie un círculo hacia atrás** (hacia la izquierda), terminando justo sobre la línea base.

 Toque debajo de la línea media e **inicie un círculo hacia atrás** (hacia la izquierda), terminando justo sobre la línea base.

 Toque la línea superior y **trace una línea recta hacia abajo** hasta la línea base. **Levante.** Toque la línea superior y **siga el trazo hacia la derecha; trace una curva hacia adelante** hasta la línea base; **siga el trazo hacia la izquierda.**

 Toque en la mitad entre la línea media y la línea base y **trace un círculo completo hacia atrás** (hacia la izquierda). **Levante.** Toque la línea superior y **trace una línea recta hacia abajo** hasta la línea base.

o

Toque en la mitad entre la línea media y la línea base y **haga un círculo completo hacia atrás** (hacia la izquierda). **Trace una línea recta hacia arriba** hasta tocar la línea superior. **Haga un trazo recto hacia abajo** hasta la línea base.

 Toque la línea superior y **trace una línea recta hacia abajo** hasta la línea base. **Pare. Siga el trazo hacia la derecha. Levante.** Toque la línea superior y **siga el trazo hacia la derecha. Levante.** Toque la línea media y **siga el trazo hacia la derecha.** Pare antes de que la línea sea del largo de las líneas anteriores.

Toque en la mitad entre la línea media y la línea base, **siga el trazo hacia la derecha; haga un círculo hacia atrás** (hacia la izquierda), terminando justo sobre la línea base.

o

Toque en la mitad entre la línea media y la línea base y **haga un círculo hacia atrás** (hacia la izquierda), terminando justo sobre la línea base. **Levante.** Toque hasta la mitad de la línea y **haga un trazo hacia la derecha.**

Toque la línea superior y **trace una línea recta hacia abajo** hasta la línea base. **Levante.** Toque la línea superior y **siga el trazo hacia la derecha. Levante.** Toque la línea media y **siga el trazo hacia la derecha.** Pare antes de que la línea sea del largo de la línea anterior.

Toque debajo de la línea superior e **inicie una curva hacia atrás** (hacia la izquierda); **trace una línea recta** hasta la línea base. **Levante.** Toque la línea media y **siga el trazo hacia la derecha.**

Toque debajo de la línea superior e **inicie una curva hacia atrás** (hacia la izquierda), terminando en la línea media. **Siga el trazo hacia la izquierda.**

Toque en la mitad entre la línea media y la línea base y **trace un círculo completo hacia atrás** (hacia la izquierda). **Levante.** Toque la línea media y **trace una línea recta hacia abajo** atravesando la línea base; **haga una curva hacia atrás** (hacia la izquierda), hasta que toque la próxima línea de escritura.

o

Toque en la mitad entre la línea media y la línea base y **haga un círculo completo hacia atrás** (hacia la izquierda). **Trace una línea recta hacia arriba** hasta tocar la línea media. **Trace una línea recta hacia abajo** atravesando la línea base y **haga una curva hacia atrás** (hacia la izquierda), hasta que toque la próxima línea.

Toque la línea superior y **trace una línea recta hacia abajo** hasta la línea base. **Levante.** Mueva a la derecha y toque la línea superior; **trace una línea recta** hasta la línea base. **Levante.** Mueva a la izquierda y toque la línea media; **haga un trazo hacia la derecha.**

Toque la línea superior y **trace una línea recta hacia abajo** hasta la línea base. **Pare.** Inicie un trazo hacia arriba y **haga una curva hacia adelante** (vuelva sobre el trazo); **continúe trazo abajo** hasta la línea base.

Toque la línea superior y **haga un trazo corto hacia la derecha. Levante.** Toque el trazo anterior en el centro y **trace una línea recta** hasta la línea base. **Levante.** Toque la línea base y **haga un trazo corto hacia la derecha.**

Toque la línea media y **trace una línea recta** hasta la línea base. **Levante.** Ponga el **punto** en la mitad entre la línea superior y la línea media.

Toque la línea superior y **trace una línea recta; trace una curva hacia adentro** (hacia la izquierda).

Toque la línea media y **trace una línea recta atravesando la línea base; trace una curva hacia atrás** (hacia la izquierda), hasta tocar la siguiente línea de escritura. **Levante.** Ponga el **punto** en la mitad entre la línea superior y la línea media.

Toque la línea superior y **trace una línea recta hacia abajo** hasta la línea base. **Levante.** Mueva a la derecha y toque la línea superior; **haga un trazo inclinado hacia la izquierda** hasta tocar la línea media. **Pare. Haga un trazo inclinado hacia la derecha** hasta tocar la línea base.

Toque la línea superior y **trace una línea recta hacia abajo** hasta la línea base. **Levante.** Mueva a la derecha y toque la línea media; **haga un trazo inclinado hacia la izquierda** hasta tocar la línea vertical en la mitad entre la línea media y la línea base. **Pare. Haga un trazo inclinado hacia la derecha** hasta tocar la línea base.

Toque la línea superior y **trace una línea recta hacia abajo** hasta la línea base. **Pare. Haga un trazo hacia la derecha.**

Toque la línea superior y **trace una línea recta hacia abajo** hasta la línea base.

Toque la línea superior y **trace una línea recta hacia abajo** hasta la línea base. **Levante.** Toque la línea superior, y **trace una línea inclinada hacia la derecha** hasta la línea base. **Levante.** Mueva a la derecha y toque la línea superior; **trace una línea inclinada hacia la izquierda** hasta la línea base. **Levante.** Toque la línea superior y **trace una línea recta** hasta la línea base.

o

Toque en línea superior y **trace una línea recta hacia abajo** hasta la línea base. **Levante.** Toque la línea superior y **haga un trazo inclinado hacia la derecha** hasta la línea base. **Haga un trazo hacia arriba inclinado hacia la derecha** hasta la línea superior. **Haga un trazo recto hacia abajo** hasta la línea base.

Toque la línea media y **trace una línea recta hacia abajo** hasta la línea base. **Pare. Inicie un trazo hacia arriba** (vuelva sobre el trazo) y **haga una curva hacia adelante** (hacia la derecha); **haga un trazo recto hacia abajo** hasta la línea base. **Pare. Inicie un trazo hacia arriba** (vuelva sobre el trazo) y **haga una curva hacia adelante** (hacia la derecha); **haga un trazo recto hacia abajo** hasta la línea base.

Toque la línea superior y **trace una línea recta hacia abajo** hasta la línea base. **Levante.** Toque la línea superior; **trace una línea inclinada hacia la derecha** hasta la línea base. **Levante.** Toque la línea superior; **trace una línea recta hacia abajo** hasta la línea base.

o

Toque la línea superior y **trace una línea recta hacia abajo** hasta la línea base. **Levante.** Toque la línea superior y **haga un trazo inclinado hacia la derecha** hasta la línea base. **Haga una línea recta hacia arriba** hasta la línea superior.

Toque la línea media y **trace una línea recta hacia abajo** hasta la línea base. **Pare. Inicie un trazo hacia arriba** (vuelva sobre el trazo) y **haga una curva hacia adelante** (hacia la derecha); **haga un trazo recto hacia abajo** hasta la línea base.

Toque la línea media y **haga un círculo completo hacia atrás** (hacia la izquierda).

Toque en la mitad entre la línea media y la línea base y **haga un círculo completo hacia atrás** (hacia la izquierda).

Toque la línea superior y **trace una línea recta hacia abajo** hasta la línea base. **Levante.** Toque la línea superior y **haga un trazo hacia la derecha; haga una curva hacia adelante** (hacia la derecha) hasta la línea media; **continúe el trazo hacia la izquierda.**

Toque la línea media y **trace una línea recta hacia abajo** atravesando la línea base hasta llegar a la próxima línea de escritura. **Levante.** Toque en la mitad entre la línea media y la línea base y **haga un círculo completo hacia adelante** (hacia la derecha).

o

Toque la línea media y **trace una línea recta hacia abajo** atravesando la línea base hasta que toque la próxima línea. **Trace una línea recta hacia arriba** hasta la mitad entre la línea base y la línea media y **haga un círculo completo hacia adelante** (hacia la derecha).

Toque la línea media y **haga un círculo completo hacia atrás** (hacia la izquierda). **Levante.** Haga un trazo corto **inclinado hacia la derecha** que termine en la línea base y atraviese el círculo en el extremo inferior derecho.

Toque en la mitad entre la línea media y la línea base y **haga un círculo completo hacia la atrás** (hacia la izquierda). **Levante.** Toque la línea media y haga un trazo recto hacia abajo atravesando la línea base; **trace un curva hacia adelante** (hasta la derecha), hasta que toque la próxima línea de escritura.

o

Toque en la mitad entre la línea media y la línea base y **haga un círculo completo hacia atrás** (hacia la izquierda). **Trace una línea recta** hasta tocar la línea media. **Trace una línea recta hacia abajo** atravesando la línea base, **haga una curva hacia adelante** (hacia la derecha), hasta que toque la próxima línea.

Toque la línea superior y **trace una línea recta hacia abajo** hasta la línea base. **Levante.** Toque la línea superior y **trace una línea hacia la derecha; trace una curva hacia adelante** (hacia la derecha) hasta la línea media; **continúe el trazo hacia la izquierda. Levante.** Toque la línea media y **haga un trazo inclinado hacia la derecha** hasta la línea base.

Toque la línea media y **trace una línea recta hacia abajo** hasta la línea base. **Pare.** Inicia un trazo hacia arriba (vuelva sobre el trazo) y **trace una curva hacia adelante** (hacia la derecha), terminando justo debajo la línea media.

Toque debajo de la línea superior y **haga una curva hacia atrás** (hacia la izquierda); **trace una curva hacia adelante** (hacia la derecha), terminando justo sobre la línea base.

Toque la línea media y **haga una curva hacia atrás** (hacia la izquierda); **trace una curva hacia adelante** (hacia la derecha), terminando justo sobre la línea base.

Toque la línea superior y **continúe el trazo hacia la derecha. Levante.** Toque en la mitad de la línea trazada y **trace una línea recta hacia abajo** hasta la línea base.

Toque en la mitad entre la línea superior y la línea media y **trace una línea recta hacia abajo** hasta la línea base. **Levante.** Toque la línea media y **continúe trazo hacia la derecha.**

Toque la línea superior y **haga una línea recta hacia abajo; curva hacia adelante** (hacia la derecha); **continúe el trazo hacia arriba** hasta la línea superior.

Toque la línea media y **haga una línea recta hacia abajo; curva hacia adelante** (hacia la derecha). **Inicie un trazo hasta la línea media. Pare. Haga una línea recta hacia abajo** (vuelva sobre el trazo) hasta la línea base.

Toque la línea superior y **trace una línea inclinada hacia la derecha** hasta la línea base. **Levante.** Mueva hacia la derecha y toque la línea superior; **trace una línea inclinada hacia la izquierda** hasta la línea base.

o

Toque la línea superior y **haga un trazo inclinado hacia la derecha** hasta la línea base. **Haga un trazo hacia arriba inclinado hacia la derecha** hasta la línea superior.

Toque la línea media y **trace una línea inclinada hacia la derecha** hasta la línea base. **Levante.** Mueva hacia la derecha y toque la línea media; **trace una línea inclinada hacia la izquierda** hasta la línea base.

o

Toque la línea media y **haga un trazo inclinado hacia la derecha** hasta la línea base. **Haga un trazo hacia arriba inclinado hacia la derecha** hasta la línea media.

Toque la línea superior y **trace una línea inclinada hacia la derecha** hasta la línea base. **Levante.** Mueva hacia la derecha y toque la línea superior; **trace una línea inclinada hacia la izquierda** hasta la línea base. **Levante.** Toque la línea superior y **trace una línea inclinada hacia la derecha** hasta la línea base. **Levante.** Mueva hacia la derecha y toque la línea superior; **trace una línea inclinada hacia la izquierda** hasta la línea base.

o

Toque la línea superior y **haga un trazo inclinado hacia la derecha** hasta la línea base. **Haga un trazo hacia arriba inclinado hacia la derecha** hasta la línea superior. **Haga un trazo inclinado hacia la derecha** hasta la línea base. **Haga un trazo hacia arriba inclinado hacia la derecha** hasta la línea superior.

Toque la línea media y **trace una línea inclinada hacia la derecha** hasta la línea base. **Levante.** Mueva hacia la derecha y toque la línea media; **trace una línea inclinada hacia la izquierda** hasta la línea base. **Levante.** Toque la línea media y **trace una línea inclinada hacia la derecha** hasta la línea base. **Levante.** Mueva hacia la derecha y toque la línea media; **trace una línea inclinada hacia la izquierda** hasta la línea base.

o

Toque la línea media y **haga un trazo inclinado hacia la derecha** hasta la línea base. **Haga un trazo hacia arriba inclinado hacia la derecha** hasta la línea media. **Haga un trazo inclinado hacia la derecha** hasta la línea base. **Haga un trazo hacia arriba inclinado hacia la derecha** hasta la línea media.

Toque la línea superior y **trace una línea inclinada hacia la derecha** hasta la línea base. **Levante.** Mueva hacia la derecha y toque la línea superior y **trace una línea inclinada hacia la izquierda** hasta la línea base.

Toque la línea media y **trace una línea inclinada hacia la derecha** hasta la línea base. **Levante.** Mueva hacia la derecha y toque la línea media y **trace una línea inclinada hacia la izquierda** hasta la línea base.

Toque la línea superior y **haga un trazo inclinado hacia la derecha** hasta la línea media. **Levante.** Mueva a la derecha y toque la línea superior; **trace una línea inclinada hacia la izquierda** hasta la línea media. **Pare. Haga una línea recta hacia abajo** hasta la línea base.

Toque la línea superior y **continúe el trazo hacia la derecha. Pare. Trace una línea inclinada hacia la izquierda** hasta la línea base. **Pare. Trace una línea hacia la derecha.**

Toque línea media y **trace una línea inclinada hacia la derecha** hasta la línea base. **Levante.** Mueva a la derecha y toque la línea media; **trace una línea inclinada hacia la izquierda** atravesando la línea base hasta la próxima línea de escritura.

Toque la línea media y **continúe el trazo hacia la derecha. Pare. Trace una línea inclinada hacia la izquierda** hasta la línea base. **Pare. Trace una línea hacia la derecha.**

Números

Toque la línea superior y **trace una línea recta hacia abajo** hasta la línea base.

Toque debajo la línea superior y **trace una curva hacia adelante** (hacia la derecha), que toque la línea superior; **haga un trazo inclinado hacia la izquierda** hasta la línea base. **Pare. Haga un trazo hacia la derecha.**

Toque debajo la línea superior y **trace una curva hacia adelante** (hacia la derecha), hacia la línea media; **trace una curva hacia adelante** (hacia la derecha) terminando sobre la línea base.

Toque la línea superior y **haga un trazo recto hacia abajo** hasta la línea media. **Pare. Haga un trazo hacia la derecha. Levante.** Toque la línea superior y **haga un trazo recto hacia abajo** hasta la línea base, cruzando el trazo horizontal.

Toque la línea superior y **haga un trazo recto hacia abajo** hasta la línea media. **Pare. Haga un círculo hacia adelante** (hacia la derecha), terminando sobre la línea base. **Levante.** Toque la línea superior y **continúe el trazo hacia la derecha.**

Toque la línea superior y **haga una curva hacia abajo** hasta la línea base; **trace una curva hacia arriba** hasta la línea media y **alrededor** para cerrar el círculo.

Toque la línea superior, **haga un trazo hacia la derecha. Pare. Haga un trazo inclinado hacia la izquierda** hasta la línea base.

Toque debajo la línea superior y **trace una curva hacia atrás** (hacia la izquierda); **trace una curva hacia adelante** (hacia la derecha), tocando la línea base. **Inicie una curva hacia arriba,** cruzando el trazo de la curva para unirlo con el trazo inicial, terminando en la línea superior.

Toque en la mitad entre la línea superior y la línea media y **haga un círculo completo hacia atrás** (hacia la izquierda). **Haga una línea recta hacia abajo** hasta la línea base.

Toque la línea superior y **trace una línea recta hacia abajo hasta la línea base. Levante.** Toque la línea superior y **haga una curva hacia abajo** hasta la línea base; **trace una curva hacia la línea superior.**

SUPPORTIVE MATERIALS

In addition to the Practice Masters, the Blackline Masters for School-Home Involvement, and other instructional supportive materials, the Teacher Resource Binder contains the following supportive materials, located in the binder pockets.

Transparencies

Guidelines Shows the headline, broken midline, red baseline, and descender space for teacher demonstration of letterforms in kindergarten through grade four.

Alphabet Both uppercase and lowercase letters in manuscript, along with the numerals.

Letter Groupings Both uppercase and lowercase letters in manuscript, grouped according to commonality of strokes.

Keys to Legibility The five keys for objectively evaluating handwriting.

Evaluation Scale Sentences Sentences the students are to write periodically for evaluating their progress.

Charts

Letter Groupings Both uppercase and lowercase letters in manuscript, along with the numerals, for placing on the wall in the writing center.

Handwriting Positions Shows correct body posture, position of the hand and arm, and position of the paper and pencil for manuscript writing (for the writing center).

Keys to Legibility The five keys for objectively evaluating handwriting (for the writing center).

Evaluation Scale Examples of children's writing from throughout the United States, ranked according to the keys to legibility.

Scope and Sequence A complete listing of the scope and sequence of skills presented in each grade of the series.

Worksheet

Contains: all the letterforms, grouped according to similarity; the keys to legibility; and a pretest to determine needs.

Peek Thru Overlays

Designed to be placed over letters that have been written to check for shape, size, and slant.

The Zaner-Bloser Handwriting

Certificate of Progress

Awarded to

_____

In recognition of outstanding progress toward the goals and standards set forth in the Zaner-Bloser Handwriting Program.

Given this _____ day of _____, 19_____.

ZANER-BLOSER HANDWRITING

_____
Grade

_____
Teacher

_____
School

B49

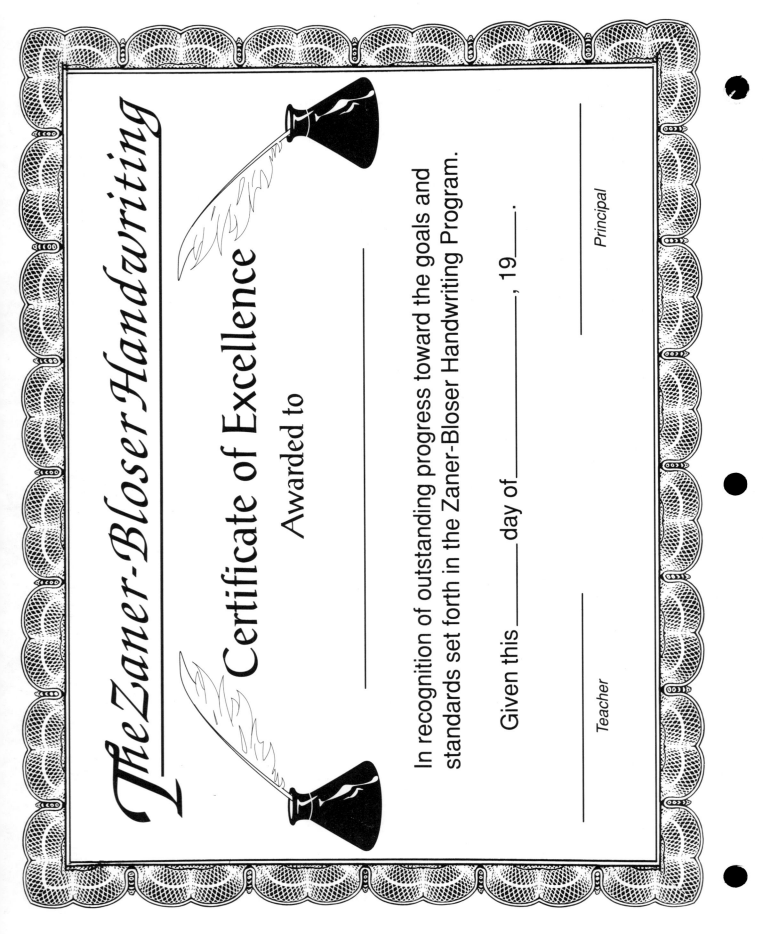

The Zaner-Bloser Handwriting

Certificate of Excellence

Awarded to

_____

In recognition of outstanding progress toward the goals and standards set forth in the Zaner-Bloser Handwriting Program.

Given this _____ day of _____, 19____.

_____
Teacher

_____
Principal

B50

SCHOOL-HOME INVOLVEMENT
ENGLISH AND SPANISH

Consistency in the skills being taught in the school and at home is an important factor in student success. These materials provide parents with correct models of letterforms, paper and pencil positions, and many other elements important to legible handwriting. Blackline masters are provided for

- a letter informing parents of the program being studied
- the Zaner-Bloser Alphabet for this grade level
- an illustration of proper pencil position
- an illustration of proper paper position
- Barbe Modality Checklist (parents) to help parents determine their own dominant learning modalities
- Barbe Modality Checklist (children 5-8, or 9 and over) to help parents determine their child's dominant learning modality

This information should be sent home at the beginning of the school year so that parents can reinforce handwriting skills throughout the year.

Worksheets are also available to help parents become familiar with the Zaner-Bloser handwriting program and to reinforce good handwriting at home (see binder pockets).

The same school-home involvement materials are provided in English and Spanish. Students and parents for whom English is a second language will find these materials helpful.

Zaner-Bloser
EDUCATIONAL PUBLISHERS

Clinton S. Hackney, Ed.D.
LANGUAGE ARTS CONSULTANT
P.O. Box 16764 • Columbus, OH 43216-6764

Dear Parent:

Your child is learning to write the Zaner-Bloser Manuscript Alphabet. This form of writing is taught before cursive writing for several very important reasons:

- Manuscript writing more closely resembles the type on the printed page; therefore, one alphabet serves for both reading and writing.
- The letters are made with straight lines and circles and are easy for the young child to learn.
- Using manuscript until the fine muscles are developed allows your child more immediate success in recording his or her own thoughts.
- Mastery of manuscript writing prepares the child for a successful and easy introduction to cursive writing.

The Zaner-Bloser Alphabet that your child is learning to write is the most widely used alphabet in today's schools. Not only is it used in the popular Zaner-Bloser handwriting programs, it is also used in practically all of the major spelling series. A copy of this alphabet is provided for you. You will want to have it readily available for reference.

Handwriting instruction strives to achieve fluent, legible writing. Effective written communication is, of course, the final goal.

Sincerely,

Clinton S. Hackney

Clinton S. Hackney, Ed.D.

Zaner-Bloser
EDUCATIONAL PUBLISHERS

Clinton S. Hackney, Ed.D.

LANGUAGE ARTS CONSULTANT

P.O. Box 16764 • Columbus, OH 43216-6764

Estimados Padres:

Su niño está aprendiendo a escribir el Alfabeto Manuscrito publicado por Zaner-Bloser. La escritura con letra manuscrita se enseña a los niños antes que la letra cursiva por varias razones importantes:

- La escritura manuscrita se asemeja más al tipo de escritura empleado en las páginas impresas; por lo tanto, el mismo alfabeto se utiliza para dos propósitos: leer y escribir.
- Las letras se forman por medio de líneas rectas y círculos, por lo tanto, son fáciles de aprender para los niños pequeños.
- Al escribir con letra manuscrita mientras se desarollan los músculos delicados del niño, le permite un éxito inmediato al escribir sus propios pensamientos.
- El dominio completo de la escritura manuscrita prepara al niño con mas éxito y le facilita la introduccion a la escritura cursiva.

El alfabeto publicado por Zaner-Bloser que su niño está aprendiendo a escribir es el alfabeto utilizado más comunmente en las escuelas de hoy dia. No solamente se usa el mismo en los programas conocidos de escritura de Zaner-Bloser, sino que también se utilizan en los programas de ortografía más importantes. Adjuntole enviamos una copia de este alfabeto para tenerlo a mano como referencia.

La enseñanza de la escritura tiene como objeto el escribir con fluidez y legibilidad. Por supuesto, la expresión por escrito en forma efectiva es, naturalmente, el objetivo final.

Respetuosamente,

Clinton S. Hackney

Clinton S. Hackney, Ed.D.

B54

Zaner-Bloser Alphabet

Kindergarten and Grade 1

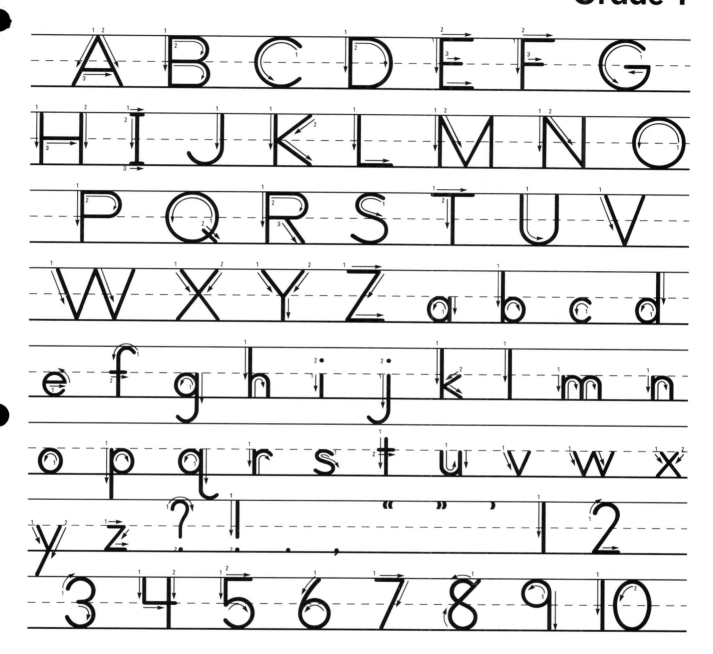

Note to Parents:

This alphabet will show you the correct formation of the letters your child is learning to write in the school handwriting program. The arrows and numerals indicate the direction and sequence of the strokes that form the letters.

The size of the letters your child is writing depends on his or her grade level. At the kindergarten level the letter size is 1⅛ inches, and at the first grade level it is ⅝ inch. In the event you wish to purchase paper for your child to practice the letter formations at home, please be sure the paper has the correct size ruled lines.

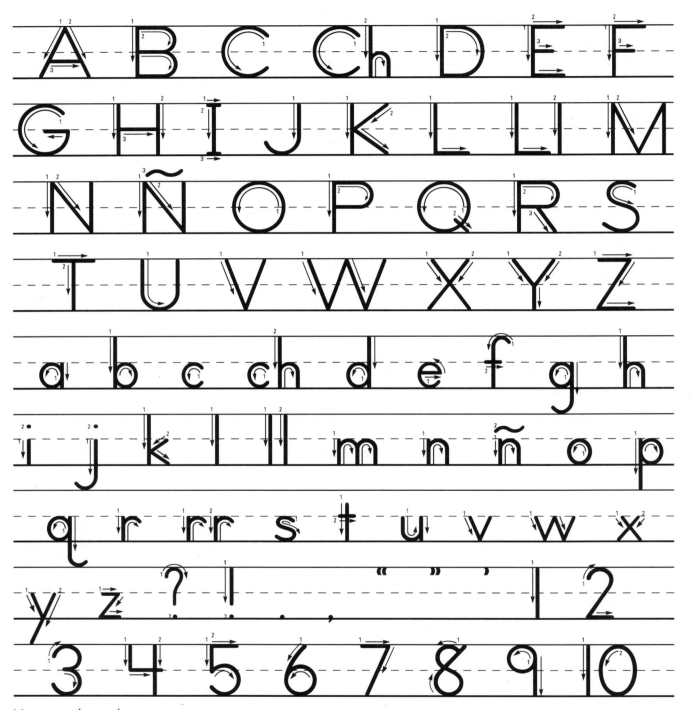

Nota para los padres:

Este alfabeto español les demuestra la formación correcta de las letras que su niño o niña está aprendiendo a escribir en la escuela. Las flechas indican la dirección y los números indican la sucesión de los trazos que forman las letras.

El tamaño de las letras que su niño o niña está escribiendo depende en el nivel o grado. En el nivel de preparación las letras miden 1⅛", y en primer grado las letras miden ⅝" de una pulgada.

El alfabeto inglés se forma por letras o signos que representan los sonidos del idioma. El alfabeto español se forma del mismo modo pero además incluye las siguientes letras: **ch, ll, ñ, rr.** La **w** no pertenece a la escritura española pero se incluye para representar los sonidos de ciertas palabras de origen extranjero.

PENCIL POSITION

LEFT HAND

POINTS TOWARD
LEFT ELBOW

PENCIL NEAR BIG KNUCKLE

HOLD THE PENCIL WITH FIRST
TWO FINGERS AND THUMB
FIRST FINGER ON TOP

BEND THUMB

LAST TWO FINGERS TOUCH PAPER

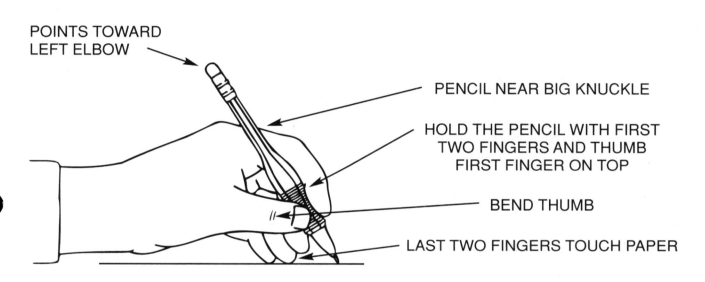

RIGHT HAND

POINTS TOWARD
RIGHT SHOULDER

PENCIL NEAR BIG KNUCKLE

HOLD THE PENCIL WITH FIRST
TWO FINGERS AND THUMB
FIRST FINGER ON TOP

BEND THUMB

LAST TWO FINGERS TOUCH PAPER

B57

PAPER POSITION
Manuscript

LEFT HAND

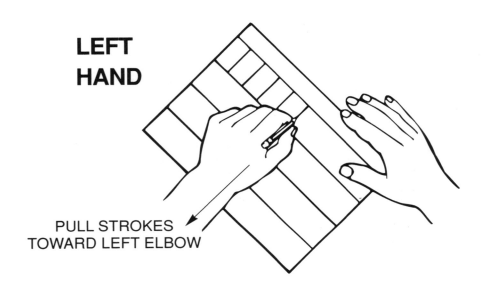

PULL STROKES
TOWARD LEFT ELBOW

RIGHT HAND

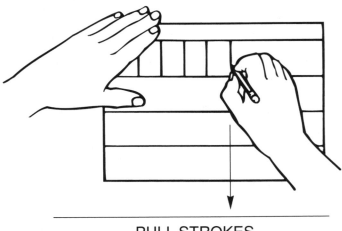

PULL STROKES
TOWARD MIDSECTION

CÓMO DEBES SUJETAR EL LÁPIZ

ZURDA O ZURDO

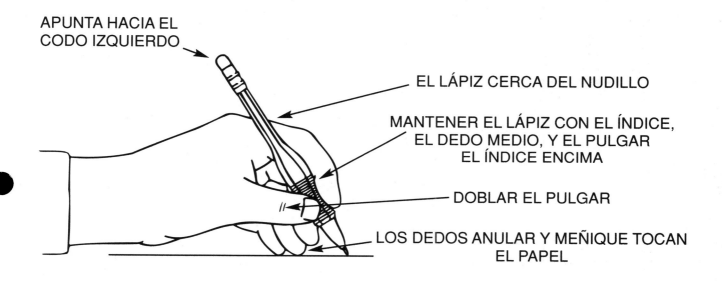

APUNTA HACIA EL CODO IZQUIERDO

EL LÁPIZ CERCA DEL NUDILLO

MANTENER EL LÁPIZ CON EL ÍNDICE, EL DEDO MEDIO, Y EL PULGAR EL ÍNDICE ENCIMA

DOBLAR EL PULGAR

LOS DEDOS ANULAR Y MEÑIQUE TOCAN EL PAPEL

DIESTRA O DIESTRO

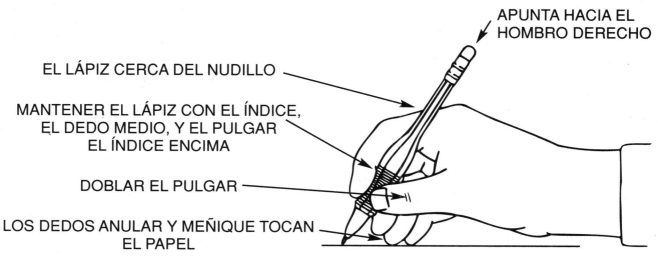

APUNTA HACIA EL HOMBRO DERECHO

EL LÁPIZ CERCA DEL NUDILLO

MANTENER EL LÁPIZ CON EL ÍNDICE, EL DEDO MEDIO, Y EL PULGAR EL ÍNDICE ENCIMA

DOBLAR EL PULGAR

LOS DEDOS ANULAR Y MEÑIQUE TOCAN EL PAPEL

B59

POSICIÓN DEL PAPEL
LA LETRA
Manuscrita

**ZURDA
O ZURDO**

HAGA UN TRAZO HACIA
EL CODO IZQUIERDO

**DIESTRA
O DIESTRO**

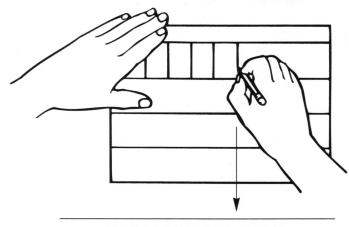

HAGA UN TRAZO HACIA
LA PARTE CENTRAL O ABDOMINAL

Barbe Modality Checklist
(Parents)
A Key to Your Own Learning Strength

Listed below are incomplete sentences, each followed by three ways of completing it. Distribute **10** points among the three phrases. Divide the **10** points according to how strongly each phrase describes you. The phrase that describes you best would get more points than the phrase that least describes you. For instance, if you believe each phrase describes you equally well, mark a *3* in two blanks and a *4* in the one that you favor even slightly more. If you are completely described by one of the phrases, mark a *10* by it and *0* by the other two. Remember, you *must* use a total of ten points for each statement.

A.	My emotions can often be interpreted from my:	___ facial expressions.	___ voice quality.	___ general body tone.
B.	I keep up with current events by:	___ reading the newspaper thoroughly when I have time.	___ listening to the radio or watching the television news.	___ reading the headlines or spending a few minutes watching the television news.
C.	If I have business to conduct, I prefer to:	___ write letters, since I then have a record.	___ telephone, since it saves time.	___ converse while doing something (such as holding a pencil, tapping my foot, etc.).
D.	When I'm angry, I usually:	___ say nothing, walk off.	___ tell others why I'm angry.	___ tense up physically.
E.	When driving, I:	___ like quiet so I can concentrate.	___ turn on the radio as soon as I enter the car.	___ shift my body position frequently to avoid getting tired.
F.	When dressing, I consider:	___ color and coordination of clothes.	___ nothing in particular, but I can explain why I picked which clothes.	___ what I will be doing and how comfortable I want to be.
G.	At a meeting, I:	___ take notes, watch people's faces.	___ enjoy discussions in which I have an opportunity to present my point of view.	___ like frequent breaks.
H.	In my spare time, I would rather:	___ watch television, go to a movie or the theater, read.	___ listen to the radio or records, attend a concert, play an instrument, talk to friends.	___ engage in physical activity of some kind (sports, handwork, etc.).
I.	Under stress, I would discipline a child by:	___ separating the child from the group, giving a stern look.	___ scolding, telling the child what he or she did wrong.	___ holding child's arm, picking child up, other physical action.
J.	When rewarding a child, I:	___ smile, give stick-ons, post child's work for others to see.	___ give oral praise to child.	___ give a hug, a pat on the back.
	Total	___ **Visual**	___ **Auditory**	___ **Kinesthetic**

Barbe Modality Checklist
(Ages 5-8)
A Key to How Your Child Learns

Listed below are incomplete sentences, followed by three ways of completing each. Distribute **10** points among the three phrases. Divide the **10** points according to how strongly each phrase describes your child. The phrase that describes your child best would receive more points than the phrase that least describes your child. For instance, if you believe each phrase describes your child equally well, mark a *3* in two blanks and a *4* in the one that favors your child even slightly more. If your child is completely described by one of the phrases, mark a *10* by it and *0* by the other two. Remember, you *must* use a total of ten points for each statement.

A.	When playing, my child:	— likes details and colorful things, peers at objects and moving things.	— likes to talk, prefers toys that make sounds.	— likes to move, climb, jump, use tools; prefers toys with moving parts.
B.	During mealtime, my child:	— eats food that looks good first, sorts by color.	— talks instead of eating, prolonging meals.	— squirms in chair, may get up and down; often puts too much in mouth.
C.	When reading or being read to, my child:	— is interested in pictures, wants to see pages.	— is concerned with sounds, asks questions.	— prefers turning pages, handling the book; doesn't sit for long period.
D.	When counting, my child:	— likes to see objects being counted.	— counts aloud, may make a song of counting.	— counts on fingers, likes to touch objects while counting.
E.	When I scold my child, he or she:	— looks away, cries.	— cries or whines, explains away fault.	— doesn't listen; avoids scolding by doing something.
F.	In more formal learning (coloring, workbooks), my child:	— tries to stay in lines, uses many colors, wants things to fit in spaces.	— asks questions, talks during work.	— works rapidly, impatient to get to next page, does not stay in lines.
G.	In group situations, my child:	— tends to be quiet, watches more than initiates.	— raises voice, talks at the same time as others.	— is either first or last in line; can't wait to get moving.
H.	When angry, my child:	— uses silent treatment, may become teary-eyes, will not look at me.	— shouts, whines.	— reacts physically, clenches fist or strikes out.
I.	I can tell when my child is happy by:	— facial expression.	— voice quality.	— body movement.
J.	When looking for encouragement or reward, my child:	— looks for a smile, must have me see accomplishment.	— needs oral praise.	— needs a hug, a pat on the back.
	Total	— **Visual**	— **Auditory**	— **Kinesthetic**

Lista de Modalidades Barbe
(Padres)
Una clave de su estilo de aprendizaje

A continuación aparecen oraciones incompletas, seguidas de tres frases distintas que permiten completarlas. Distribuya **10** puntos entre las tres frases. Asigne los **10** puntos de acuerdo a cómo cada frase le describe a usted. La frase que mejor le describa debe recibir más puntos que la que peor le describa. Por ejemplo, si usted cree que las tres frases le describen igualmente bien, escriba *3* en dos de los espacios en blanco y *4* junto a la frase que le parece un poquito más acertada. Si una de las tres frases le describe perfectamente, escriba *10* junto a elle y *0* junto a las otras dos. Recuerde, tiene que usar un total de *10* puntos en cada oración.

A.	A menudo es posible interpretar mis emociones por mi:	— expresión facial.	— tono de voz.	— gestos y postura.
B.	Me mantengo al día sobre los acontecimientos actuales:	— leyendo el periódico completamente cada vez que tengo tiempo.	— escuchando la radio o mirando las noticias en la televisión.	— leyendo los titulares de los periódicos, observando las noticias en la televisión por unos cuantos minutos.
C.	Si tengo que ocuparme de algún negocio, prefiero:	— escribir cartas, puesto que entonces tengo un comprobante de lo dicho.	— hablar por teléfono, puesto que ahorra mucho tiempo.	— conversar, mientras hago algo (por ejemplo, sujetar un lápiz, marcar el compás con el pie, etc.).
Ch.	Cuando tengo un disgusto, generalmente:	— no digo nada y salgo a caminar un rato.	— explico a los demás lo que me ha disgustado.	— me lleno de tensión.
D.	Mientras manejo:	— me gusta el silencio para concentrarme.	— enciendo el radio, en cuanto subo al carro.	— cambio frecuentemente de postura para no cansarme.
E.	Al vestirme:	— me interesa el color y la coordinación de las prendas de vestir.	— no me preocupo de nada en particular, pero puedo explicar mi elección de cada prenda.	— me interesa lo qué voy a hacer y lo cómoda que me voy a sentir.
F.	En una reunión, yo:	— tomo notas, observo los rostros de las demás personas.	— disfruto de las discusiones en las cuales tengo oportunidad de presentar mi punto de vista.	— me gustan los descansos frecuentes.
G.	En mi tiempo libre, perfiero:	— mirar la televisión, ir al cino o al teatro, leer.	— oír la radio o escuchar discos, ir a conciertos, tocar un instrumento, conversar con amigos.	— dedicarma a alguna actividad física (deportes, trabajos manuales, etc.).
H.	Bajo tension, disciplinaría a un niño:	— separándolo del grupo mirándolo con enojo.	— regañándolo, explicándole qué es lo que ha hecho mal.	— sujetándolo del brazo, cargándolo en el aire, o realizaría alguna otra acción física.
I.	Para premiar a un niño:	— le sonrío, le regalo sellos, coloco su trabajo donde otros puedan verlo.	— le felicito oralmente.	— le doy un abrazo, o una palmadita en la espalda.
	Total	— **Visual**	— **Auditivo**	— **Kinestético**

Lista de Modalidades Barbe
(de 5 a 8 años)
Una clave de cómo su hijo o hija aprende

A continuación aparecen oraciones incompletas, sequidas de tres frases distintas que permiten completarlas. Distribuya **10** puntos entre las tres frases. Asigne los **10** puntos de acuerdo a cómo cada frase describe a su hijo o hija. La frase que mejor le describa debe recibir más puntos que la que peor le describa. Por ejemplo, si usted cree que las tres frases describen a su hijo or hija igualmente bien, escribe *3* en dos de los espacios en blanco y *4* junto a la frase que le parece un poquito más acertada. Si una de las tres frases describe perfectamente a su hijo o hija, escriba *10* junto a ella y *0* junto a las otras dos. Recuerde, tiene que usar un total de *10* puntos en cada oración.

A.	Cuando juega, mi hijo o hija:	__ le gustan las cosas que tienen muchos colores y detalles, y le presta atención a los objetos que se mueven.	__ le gusta hablar, prefiere los juguetes con sonido.	__ le gusta moverse, trepar, saltar, usar herramientas; prefiere los juguetes que tienen piezas movibles.
B.	Durante las comidas, mi hija o hijo:	__ come primero las cosas más atracti-vas, distribuye los ali-mentos según su color.	__ habla en vez de comer, prolonga las comidas.	__ se retuerce en la silla, a veces se levanta; a menudo pone demasiada comida en la boca.
C.	Cuando lee, o cuando le leen, mi hijo o hija:	__ se interesa en las ilustraciones, quiere ver las páginas.	__ se interesa en los sonidos, hace preguntas.	__ prefiere pasar las páginas, coger el libro; no se sienta por mucho tiempo.
Ch.	Cuando cuenta, mi hija o hijo:	__ desea ver los objetos que cuenta.	__ cuenta en voz alta, a veces cuenta cantando.	__ cuenta con los dedos, le gusta tocar los objetos que cuenta.
D.	Cuando regaño a mi hijo o hija:	__ mira hacia otra parta, llora.	__ llora o lloriquea, trata de explicar lo que ha pasado.	__ no escucha; evita el regaño haciendo algo.
E.	Durante el apren-dizaje más formal (al dibujar, al escribir en cuader-nos), mi hija o hijo:	__ trata de mantenerse dentro de la línea, usa muchos colores, quiere que las cosas quepan en los espacios.	__ hace preguntas, hable mientras trabaja.	__ trabaja rapid-amente, se impacienta por pasar a la página si-guiente, no se queda dentro de las líneas.
F.	Cuando se encuentra en un grupo, mi hijo o hija:	__ tienda a estar quieto o quieta, observa con más frecuencia que inicia.	__ levanta la voz, habla al mismo tiempo que los demás.	__ siempre está al prin-cipio o al final de la fila; no puede esperar a moverse.
G.	Cuando se enfada, mi hija o hijo:	__ se queda en silencio, quizá se le llenan los ojos de lágrimas, pero no me mira.	__ grita, lloriquea.	__ reacciona físi-camente, levanta el puño pega.
H.	Sé cuando mi hijo o hija se siente feliz, por su:	__ expresión facial.	__ tono de voz.	__ gestos y postura.
I.	Cuando busca estímulo o recono-cimiento, mi hija o hijo:	__ espera una sonrisa, quiere que yo vea su triunfo.	__ necesita recono-cimiento oral.	__ necesita un abrazo, una palmadita en la espalda.
	Total	__ **Visual**	__ **Auditivo**	__ **Kinestético**

PRACTICE MASTERS

V

Handwriting practice masters in grade 1 focus on the manuscript alphabet, recognizing shapes, discriminating sizes, recognizing letters, practicing basic strokes, and writing letters and numerals.

You may also wish to provide each student with diagrams of proper pencil and paper positions. These blackline masters are provided in the School-Home Involvement section of this binder.

Handabets are blackline masters presenting both the lowercase and the uppercase alphabets with numerical stroke counts. These masters can be reproduced (preferably on heavy construction paper or oaktag) to create alphabet flash cards.

Alphabet Fun is an activity for students who have mastered the letterforms.

HIDDEN PICTURES

Find these hidden pictures in the big picture.

feather   spoon   fish   scissors

candle   mouse   flower   egg   pear

heart   top   pencil   spool of thread   candy cane

Name

Match the picture on the left to the picture on the right.

3

Name

Look at each animal on the left. Draw a line to its shadow on the right.

4

Name

Draw lines to match the shapes.

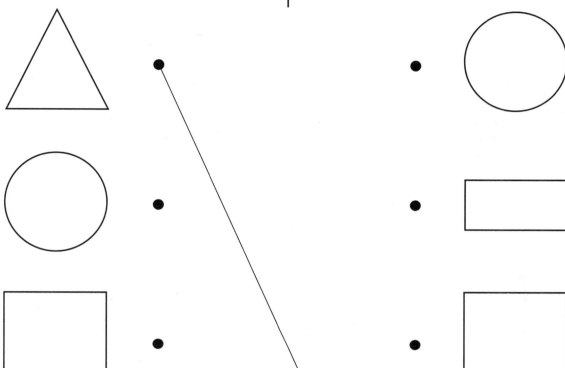

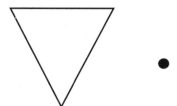
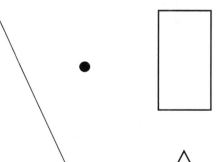
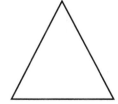
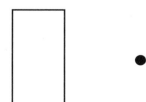
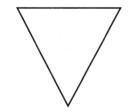

Draw a line under the two letters in each box that are the same.

G C G O Q D

r m n r h t

p q g b p f

t f k E l t

p b d o b a

6

Name

One of the letters in each row is the same as the boxed letter. Circle it.

Boxed						
i	I	I	L	i	l	t
L	I	I	L	i	l	E
w	m	w	M	u	u	n
u	n	n	m	v	u	w

Circle the two letters in each box that are the same.

| Q | O | C | Q | D |

| v | w | m | w | x |

| o | a | d | p | a |

| k | x | z | k | t |

| l | m | h | n | h |

| g | p | q | p | d |

One of the letters in each row is the same as the boxed letter. Circle it.

b	b	q	g	p
p	p	b	q	p	g
b	d	p	g	q	b
g	q	b	p	g	g

9

Trace and write the top to bottom strokes.

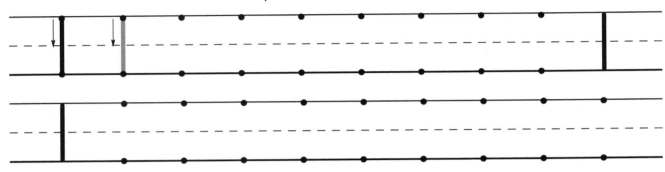

Write the top to bottom strokes to finish this picture.

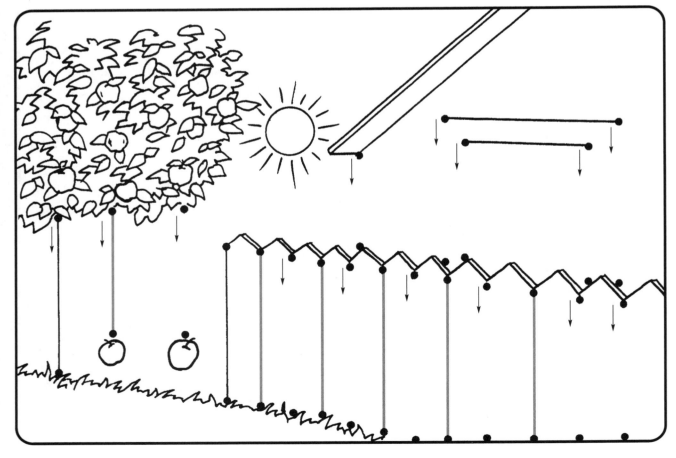

Name

Trace and write the top to bottom strokes to match the pictures.

11

Trace and write the left to right strokes to match the pictures.

 →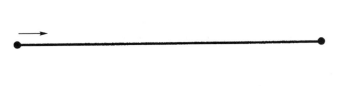

 →

Trace and write the left to right strokes to match the pictures.

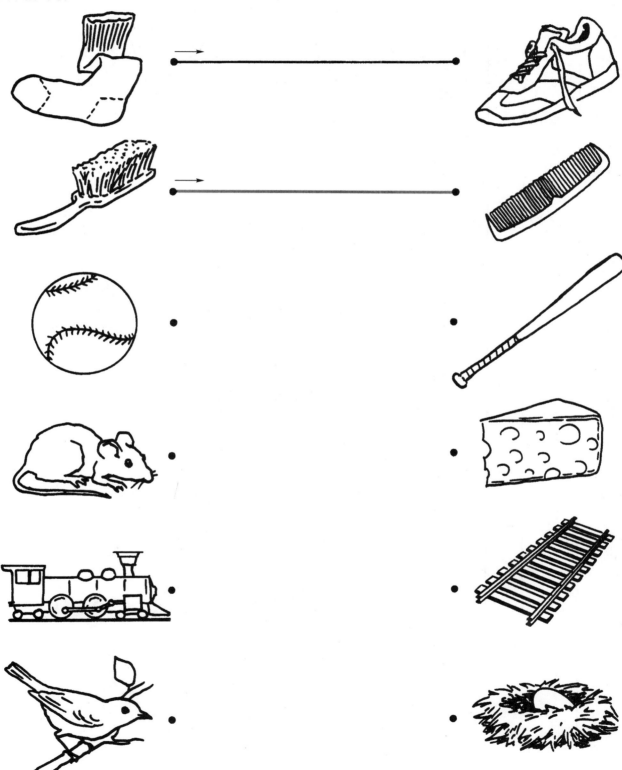

Name

Find the circles in this picture. Trace the circles using a backward motion.

Name

Trace and write the backward circles.

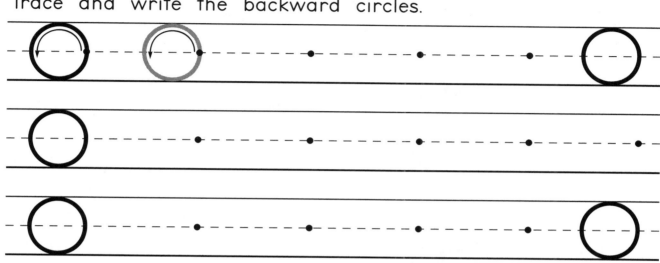

Make backward spirals. Stay between the lines.

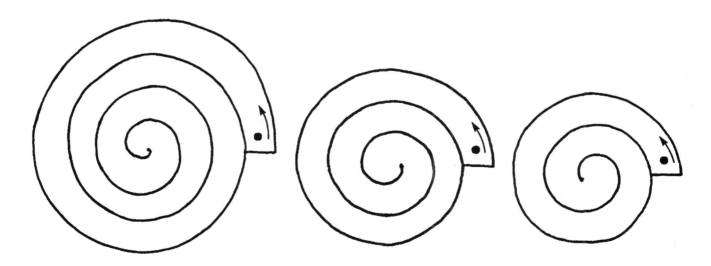

15

Name

Find the circles in this picture. Trace the circles using a forward motion.

Trace and write the forward circles.

Make forward spirals. Stay between the lines.

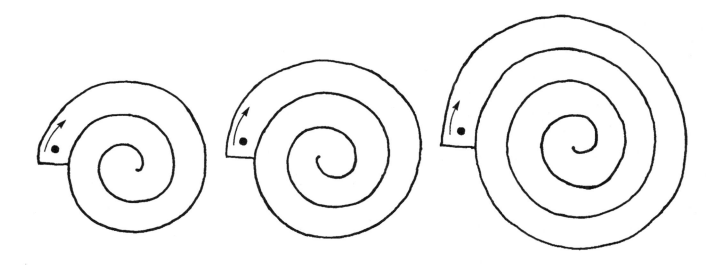

Trace and write the slant right strokes.

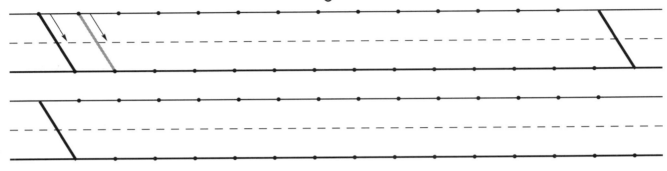

Trace the slant right strokes in this picture.

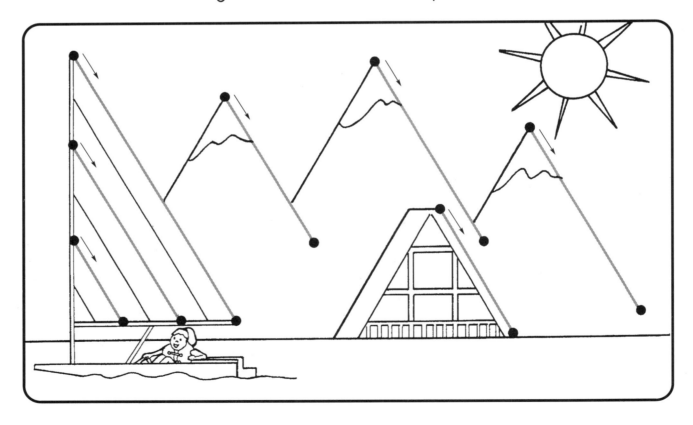

Trace and write the slant left strokes.

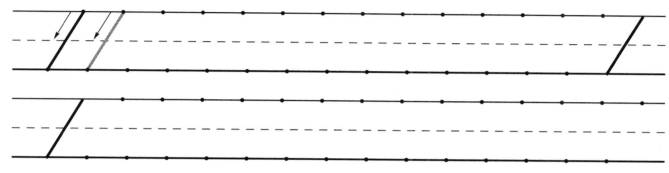

Trace the slant left strokes in this picture.

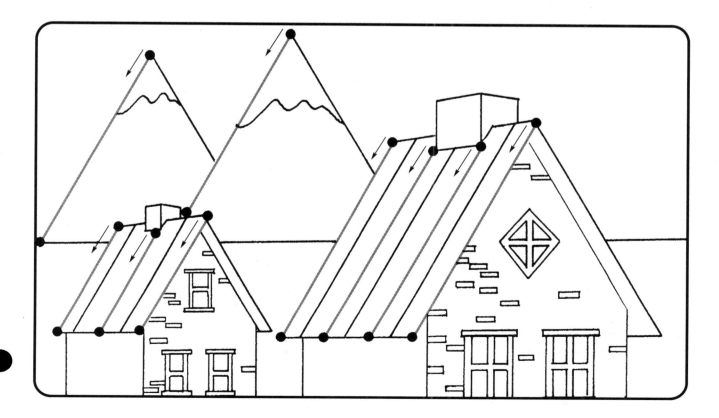

Name

Trace and write.

l l

l

l

lap ap ap ap

let et et et

like ike ike ike

lace ace ace ace

life ife ife ife

still sti_ sti_ sti_

Trace and write.

i i i i

i i

i i

wish w_sh w_sh

hive h_ve h_ve h_ve

line _ne _ne _ne

his h_s h_s h_s

time t_me t_me

hike h_ke h_ke h_ke

Trace and write.

t   t   t   t

t

t   t

that ha ha ha

trot ro ro ro

thin hn hn hn

this hs hs hs

stir s r s r s r

tub ub ub ub

HIDDEN LETTERS

l	i	t

Find these lowercase letters in the picture below.

23

Trace and write.

o o _ _ _ _ _ _ o

o _ _ _ _ _ _ _ _

o _ _ _ _ _ _ _ _ o

moon m_ _n m_ _n

only _ny _ny _ny

stool s_ _ _ s_ _ _

room r_ _m r_ _m

spoon sp_ _n sp_ _n

soon s_ _n s_ _n

Trace and write.

a a _ _ _ _ _ _ _ _ _ _ a

a _ _ _ _ _ _ _ _ _ _ _ _ _ _

a _ _ _ _ _ _ _ _ _ _ _ _ a

ant n n n

hat h h h

mat m m m

and nd nd nd

ape pe pe pe

are re re re

Trace and write.

d   d   d   d

d

d   d

dad

den   _en   _en   _en

did

bud   bu_   bu_   bu_

dot

deed   _ee_   _ee_

26

HIDDEN LETTERS

l i t o a d

Find these lowercase letters in the picture below.

27

Trace and write.

c c _ _ _ _ _ c

can _n _n _n

cut _u _u _u

cat

cub _ub _ub _ub

came _me _me

cab _b _b _b

cone _ne _ne

creek _reek _reek

Name

Trace and write.

e e _ _ _ _ _ _ _ e

keep k p k p

see s s s

fed f f f

bed b b b

set s s s

seed s s

beet b b

feel f f f

Trace and write.

f f _____ f

stiff s_____ s____

feed

fun _un _un _un

feet

fast __s_ __s_

frog _r g _r g

fed

fix _x _x _x

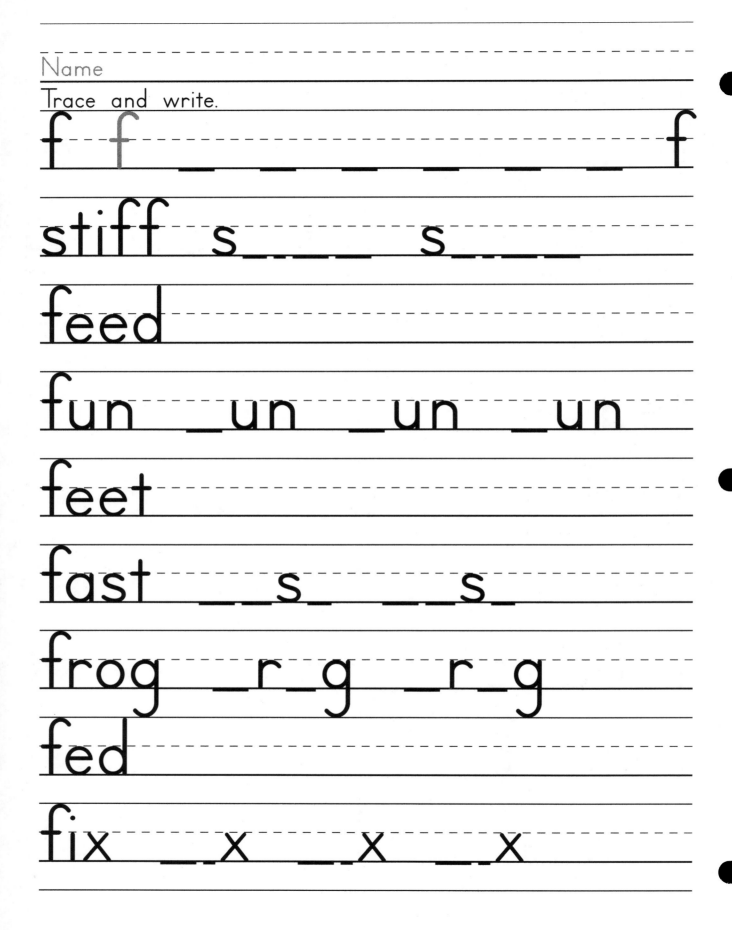

HIDDEN LETTERS

l i t o a d c e f

Find these lowercase letters in the picture below.

l i t o a d c e f

Trace and write.

l _____

i _____

t _____

o _____

a _____

d _____

c _____

e _____

f _____

live ____ v ____ wn

town ____ wn

city ____ y ____

Jill ____ J ____

road ____ r ____

far ____ r ____

Write the words.

Jill lives on a farm.

J _____ v s _____ n _____ rm.

The cat ate the food.

Th _____ h _____

Jeff left his coat.

J _____ h s _____

33

Keys to Legibility
Size

Circle the tall letters.

l	i	t	o	a	d	c	e	f

Circle the middle letters.

l	i	t	o	a	d	c	e	f

Circle the short letters.

l	i	t	o	a	d	c	e	f

Write the words.

little   tall

Name

Keys to Legibility
Size

Circle the tall letter.

| g | j | q | u | s | b | p |

Circle the middle letter.

| g | j | q | u | s | b | p |

Circle the short letters.

| g | j | q | u | s | b | p |

Circle the descenders.

| g | j | q | u | s | b | p |

Trace and write.

g g – – – – – g

get

hug hu_ hu_ hu_

gate

ago

dig

big b_ b_ b_

got

grin _rn _rn _rn

Trace and write.

j j — — — — — — j

jet

job b b b

jot

jay y y y

jog

jam m m

join n n n

joke k k

Trace and write.

q   q   _ _ _ _ _   _ _ _ _ _   q

quack   _u_ k   _u_ k

quit   _u_   _u_   _u_

quiz   _uz   _uz   _uz

quill   _u_ _   _u_ _   _u_ _

square   s_u_r_ _ _ _ _ _ _ _ _ _

queen   _u_ n   _u_ n

quilt   _u_ _   _u_ _

quite   _u_ _   _u_ _

HIDDEN LETTERS

g j q

Find these lowercase letters in the picture below.

JERI SIMKUS

Trace and write.

u u _ _ _ _ u

but b_ b_ b_

us _s _s _s _s

use _s _s _s_

tug

rug r_ r_ r_

bus b_s b_s b_s

must m_s_ m_s_

up _p _p _p _p

Trace and write.

s s ____ ____ ____ ____ s

sits

she h ____ h ____ h ____

so

dish ____ h ____ h ____ h

side

mess m ____ m ____

sit

spin ____ p _ n ____ p _ n ____ p _ n

41

HIDDEN LETTERS

g j q u s

Find these lowercase letters in the picture below.

Trace and write.

b   b ‐ ‐ ‐ ‐ ‐ ‐   b

bit

bad

bug

bag

bib

bone __n_ __n_

best

bite

Trace and write.

p p — — — — p p

pop

pumps — m — —

pup

spin — — n — — n — — n

pet

pen — n — n — n

plum — m — m

path — — h — — h

HIDDEN LETTERS

g j q u s b p

Find these lowercase letters in the picture below.

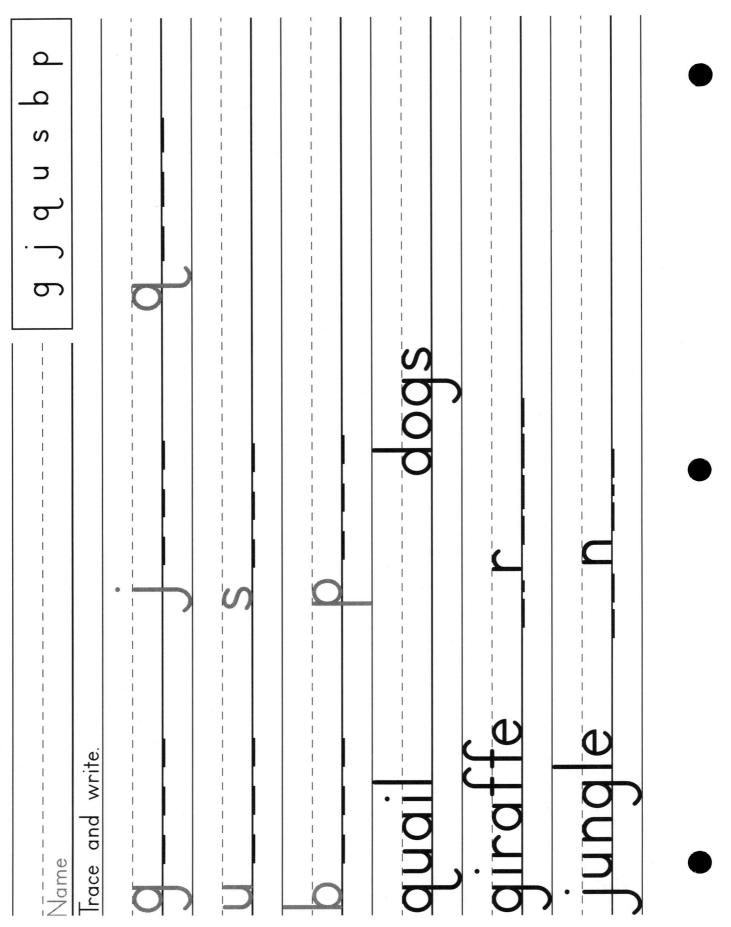

g j q u s b p

Trace and write.

g g

j j

u s

b p

quail

t r

giraffe

dogs

j n

jungle

46

Name

Write the words.

The goats jumped.

Th_____ m_____

His pig squealed.

H_____

Her pony is black.

H___ ny _____

47

For use with left-handed students.

Name

Keys to Legibility
Slant (Vertical Quality)

Paper Position
left hand

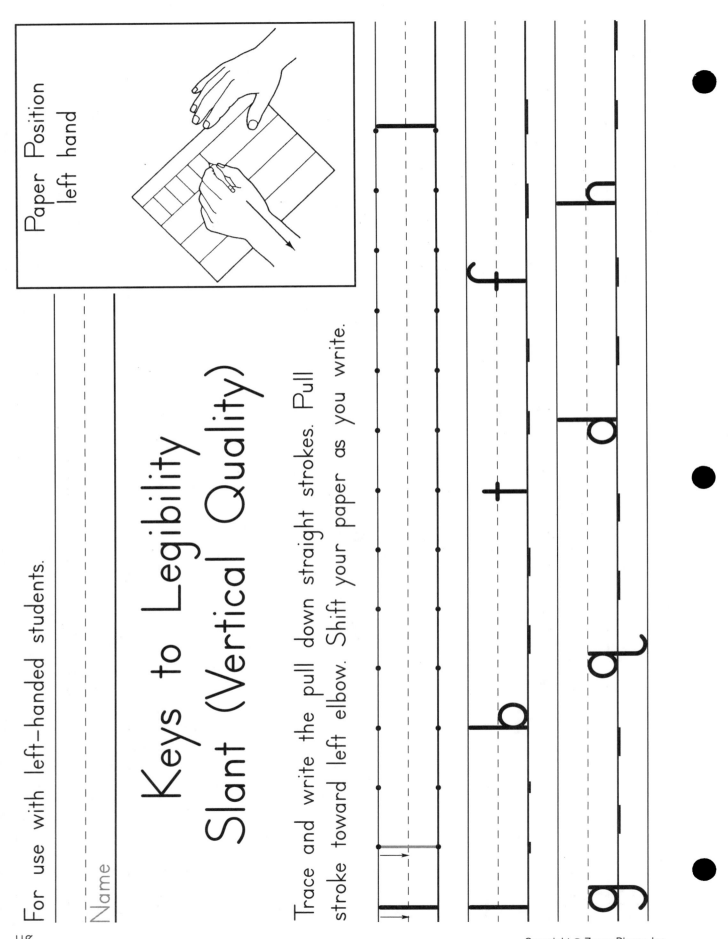

Trace and write the pull down straight strokes. Pull stroke toward left elbow. Shift your paper as you write.

b   t   f

g   q   p   h

48

For use with right-handed students.

Name

Keys to Legibility
Slant (Vertical Quality)

Trace and write the pull down straight strokes. Pull stroke toward midsection. Shift your paper as you write.

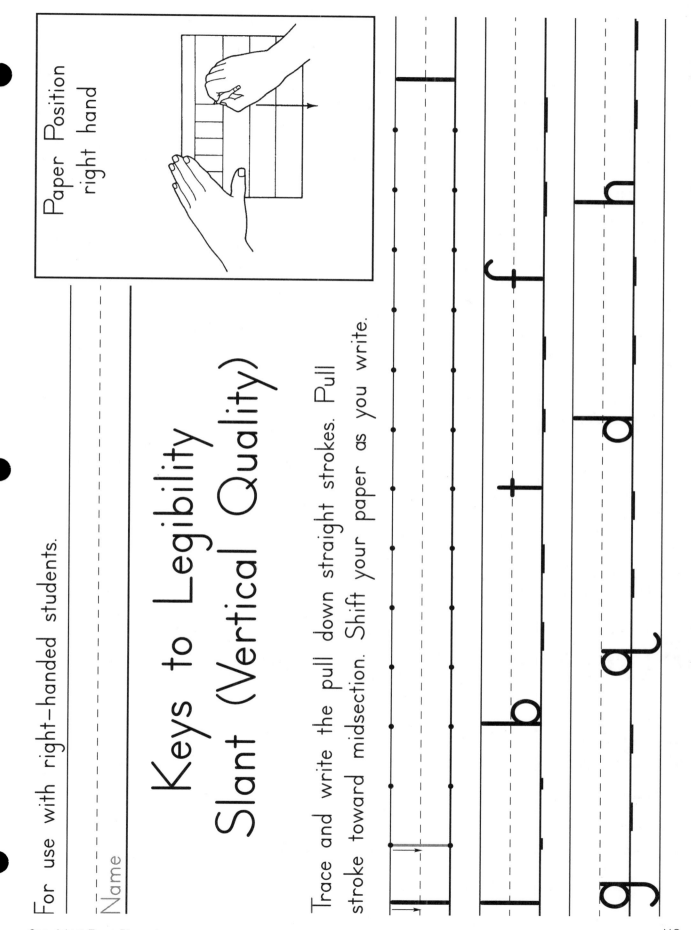

Paper Position right hand

Trace and write.

r r — — — — — r r

rose

ride

ran __n __n __n

rust

rice

run __n __n __n

rest

rake __k __k

Name

Trace and write.

n n ___ ___ ___ ___ n

nose

nut

neck __k __k

net

not

note

name __m_ __m_

then _h_ _h_

Trace and write.

m m ___ ___ ___ m

mom

met

man

mine

made

me

make __ k ___ __ k_

men

Trace and write.

h h ——————— h

has

push

the

hop

bath

hum

hush

he

Trace and write.

r

m   n   h

meals

breakfast

lunch

. dinner

54

Name

Write the words.

carrots and lima beans

peaches and pears

oranges and apples

Trace and write.

v   v _   _   _   _   _   _ v

vase

vest

stove

hive

gave

vine

van

visit

56

Trace and write.

y y — — — — — y
y

yes

yet

you

easy

hay

body

yell

yellow ——————— w

Trace and write.

w w _ _ _ _ _ w

twins

was

wish

with

show

wet

wag

sweep

58

HIDDEN LETTERS

r n m h v y w

Find these lowercase letters in the picture below.

neva Schultz

59

Trace and write.

k k _ _ _ _ _ _ _ k

skip

lake

bake

kite

bike

duck

wake

back

Name

Trace and write.

x   x   _ _ _ _ _ _ _   x

fix

fox

box

mix

ax

six

except

exact

Trace and write.

z z z _ _ _ _ _ z

zoo

zip

fuzz

buzz

fizz

zoom

breeze

puzzle

62

HIDDEN LETTERS r n m h v y w k x z

Find these lowercase letters in the picture below.

Write the missing letters.

a   d   e

k   p   r

u   y

Write the lowercase letters that have a "pull down straight" in them.

64

Write the missing letters.

c   f   g

j   m   n

s   t   w   q

Write the lowercase letters that have a circle or part of a circle in them.

Match the number of objects on the left to the same number of objects on the right by drawing a line.

66

Match the number of objects on the left to the same number of objects on the right by drawing a line.

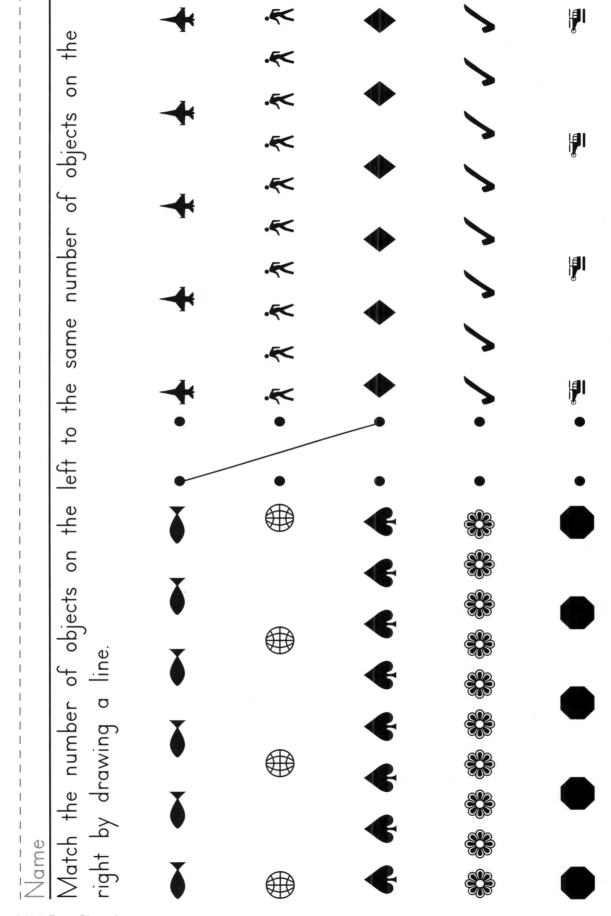

Trace and write.

I I

one

I dog

I cat

I bird

I duck

I cow

I horse

I lion

Trace and write.

2 2 _ _ _ _ _ _ 2

two

2 cars

2 pins

2 cups

2 eyes

2 bikes

2 books

2 rings

Trace and write.

3 3   3

three

3 pens

3 days

3 bees

3 balls

3 dimes

3 clocks

3 vines

Name

Trace and write.

4   4   _ _ _ _ _ _   4

four

4 bugs

4 rugs

4 cards

4 straws

4 hills

4 rakes

4 rocks

Trace and write.

5 5 _ _ _ _ _ _ 5

five

5 doors

5 drums

5 wigs

5 names

5 kings

5 keys

5 limes

Trace and write.

6 6 — — — — — — 6

six

6 pups

6 men

6 cubs

6 beds

6 pigs

6 tires

6 desks

73

Trace and write.

7 7 — — — — — — 7

seven

7 girls

7 suns

7 boys

7 trucks

7 sails

7 hats

7 quilts

Name

Trace and write.

8 8 _ _ _ _ _ _ _ 8

eight

8 cooks

8 camels

8 bears

8 cabs

8 colors

8 boats

8 lamps

Trace and write.

9   9 — — — — — — — — — — — — — — — — 9

nine

9   clouds

9   stars

9   lines

9   circles

9   shapes

9   faces

9   tacks

Trace and write.

10 10 _ _ _ 10

ten

10 logs

10 trees

10 nets

10 nuts

10 nests

10 pies

10 nails

Name

Trace and write the numerals.

1

2

3

4

5

Name

Trace and write the numerals.

6   6   6

7   7   7

8   8   8

9   9   9

10 10 10

Pencil Position
left hand

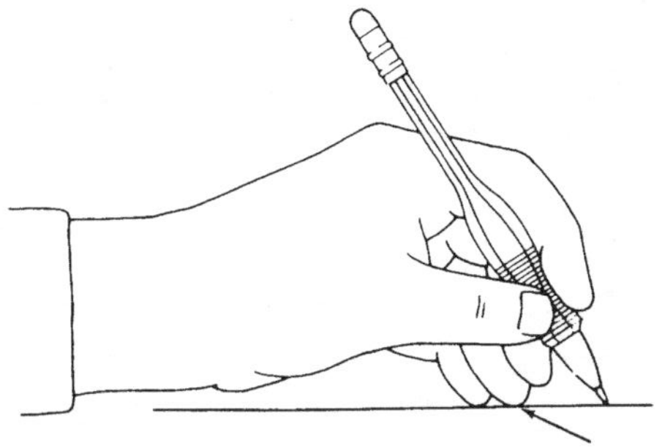

Keys to Legibility
Smoothness (Line Quality)

Be sure that your lines are even.

Correct

Incorrect

smooth

smooth

Write the words.

line

pencil

Pencil Position
right hand

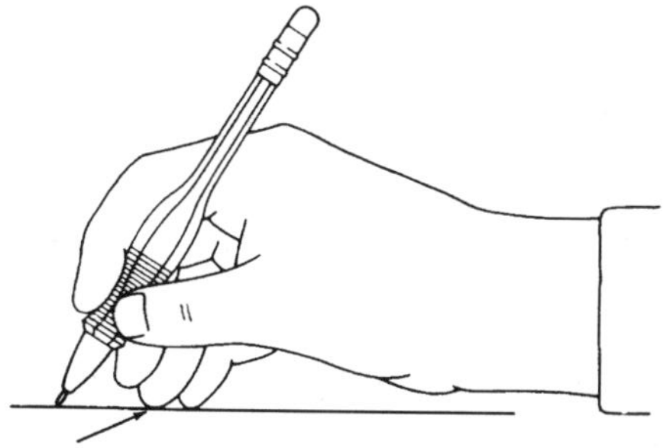

Keys to Legibility
Smoothness (Line Quality)

Be sure that your lines are smooth.

Correct   Incorrect

even   even

Write the words.

light   dark

Checkpoint   My writing is smooth.   ☐ Yes ☐ No

Match the uppercase letters to the lowercase letters.

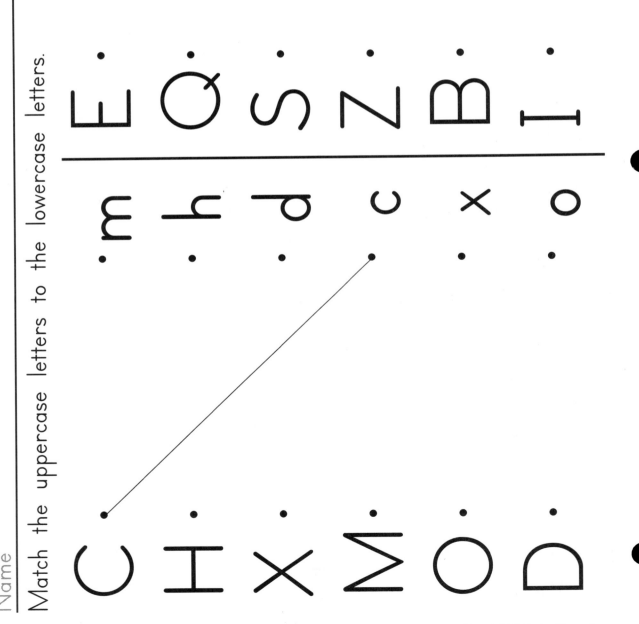

Match the uppercase letters to the lowercase letters.

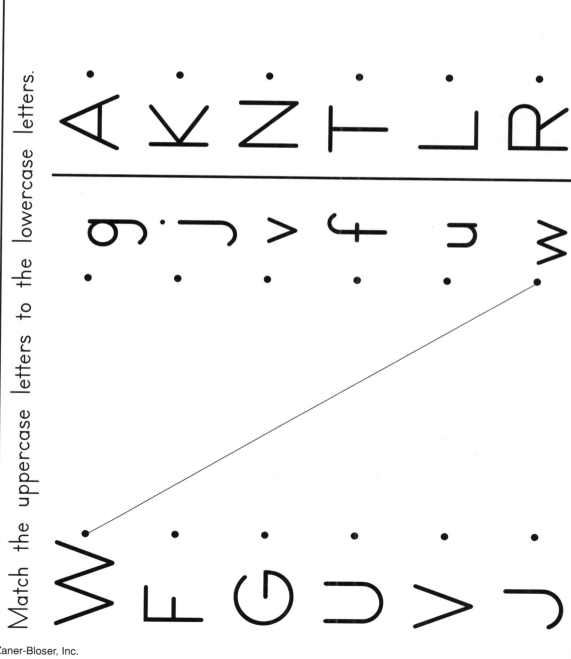

83

Trace and write.

L L _ _ _ _ L

Lana

Lara

Lee

Lars

Les

Leah

Leo listens well.

Trace and write.

I I _____ I

Iris

Inez

Ivan

Igor

Irene

Irma

I sat down.

Name

Trace and write.

T T   T

Tara

Tami

Tanya

Toby

Tracy

Thad

They woke up.

HIDDEN LETTERS

L I T

Find these uppercase letters in the picture below.

Trace and write.

E E E   E

Erin

Eva

Earl

Ellis

Evan

Edna

Everyone sang.

88

Trace and write.

F F   F

Fern

Faye

Flo

Freda

Fritz

Flora

Frank swam.

Trace and write.

H H H — — — — H

Helen

Holly

Heidi

Hugh

Hank

Hatti

He laughed loudly.

HIDDEN LETTERS

L I T E F H

Find these uppercase letters in the picture below.

Trace and write.

O O ___ ___ ___ O

Olga

Otis

Oren

Ola

Owen

Ohio

Otto played first.

Trace and write.

Q Q Q _ _ _ Q

Queenie

Quincy

Quint

Quinn

Quilla

Quinta

Quinten slept.

Trace and write.

C C C   C

Cleo

Carol

Cara

Carl

Cher

Chad

Cliff smiled at me.

Trace and write.

G   G _ _ _ _ G

Gena

Gina

Gale

Gene

Gert

Glen

Gus looked happy.

Trace and write.

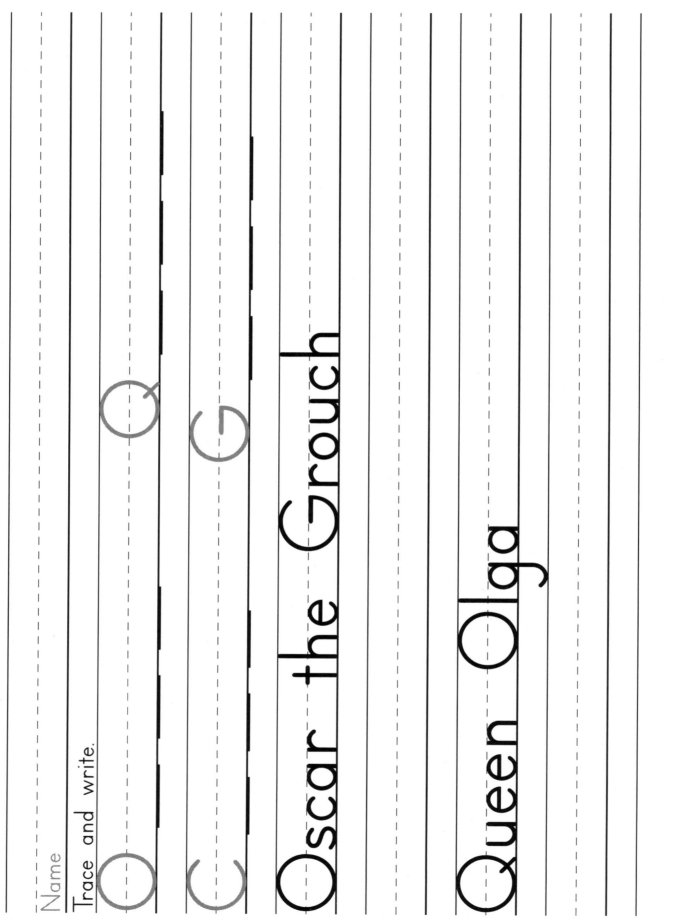

Qq

Gg

Oscar the Grouch

Queen Olga

Name

Trace and write.

Chicago

Quebec

Oklahoma City

Garden City

Show students how to draw these figures, beginning with the letterforms.

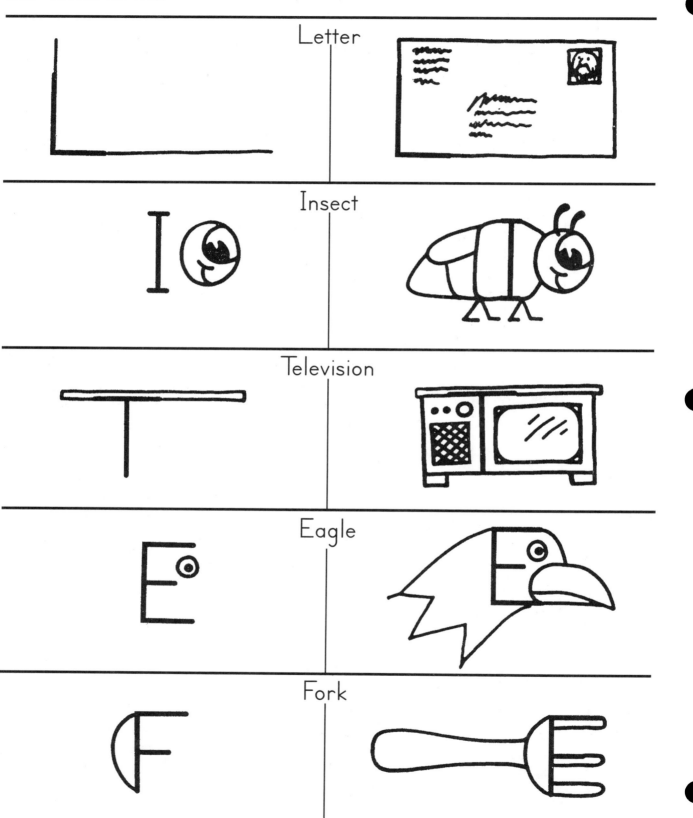

Letter

Insect

Television

Eagle

Fork

Show students how to draw these figures, beginning with the letterforms.

House	
Octopus	
Queen	
Canoe	
Guitar	

Keys to Legibility

Spacing

Write the words.

a | on

book

This is good spacing.

my new bike

Checkpoint   My spacing is correct.   ☐ Yes ☐ No

Keys to Legibility
Shape

Write the words. Be sure that your circles are closed.

old

baby

balloon

dinosaur

Checkpoint   My circles are closed.   ☐ Yes ☐ No

Name

Trace and write.

P P   P

Pam

Pat

Pearl

Paul

Phil

Perry

Please hurry.

Trace and write.

R R _____ R

Rita

Ruth

Ray

Rex

Rick

Reed

Rick ran faster.

Trace and write.

B B _ _ _ B

Bev

Becky

Brad

Ben

Bob

Beth

Bees make honey.

Trace and write.

D D ——— ——— D

Dawn

Dave

Don

Dan

Dora

Dick

Dora's dog barks.

Trace and write.

P   R

B   D

Paul can jump.

Brenda bought books.

Name _____

Write the sentences.

Ryan ran home.

Denise has a cat.

Babies drink milk.

Trace and write.

U U U

Ulysses

Ursula

Utah

Ursa

Uda

Uri

Una ran home.

Trace and write.

S S _ _ _ _ _ _ _ _ _ S

Sue

Sally

Sam

Scott

Skip

Sean

She sat with Sue.

Trace and write.

J J J   J

Jane

Jill

John

Jack

Joan

Joy

Joel watched us.

Name

HIDDEN LETTERS P R B D U S J

Find these uppercase letters in the picture below.

Jeri Simkus

Trace and write.

A A A ___ ___ ___ A

Amy

Ann

Adam

Abby

Alan

Abel

Aldo ate the apple.

Name

Trace and write.

N N N ——— N

Nora

Nan

Neal

Ned

Nick

Noel

Nate walks fast.

Name

Trace and write.

M M M   M

Mae

Mary

Mike

Mark

Meg

Missy

Mom hugs me.

HIDDEN LETTERS

$\boxed{\text{P R B D U S J A N M}}$

Find these uppercase letters in the picture below.

Show students how to draw these figures, beginning with the letterforms.

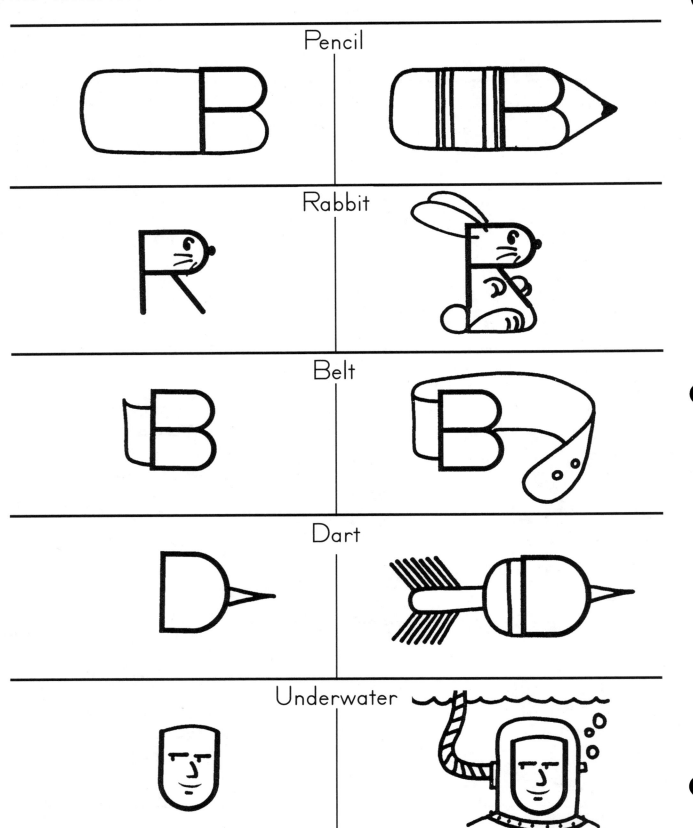

Pencil

Rabbit

Belt

Dart

Underwater

Show students how to draw these figures, beginning with the letterforms.

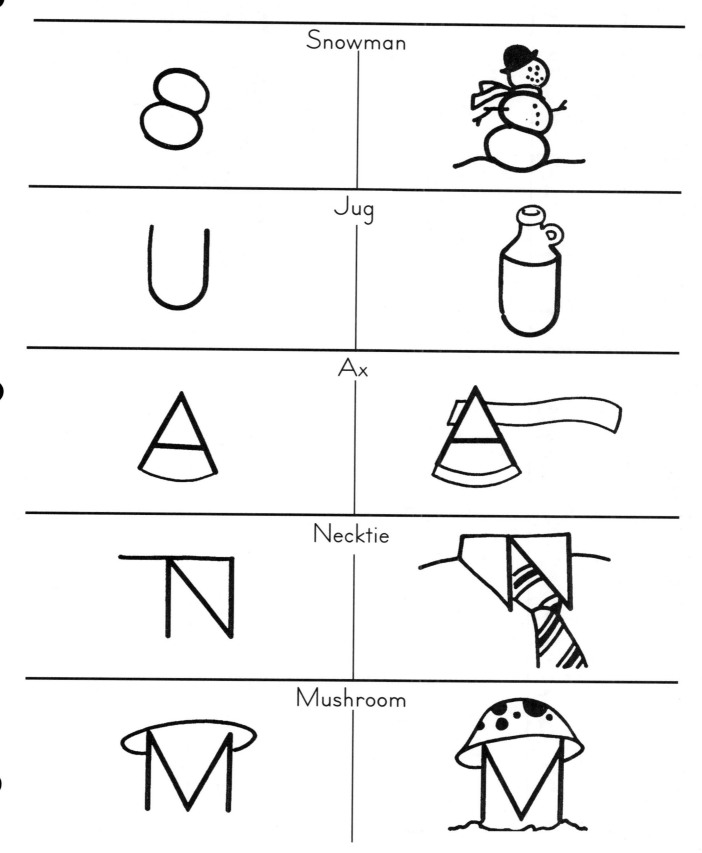

Snowman

Jug

Ax

Necktie

Mushroom

Review—Keys to Legibility

Write the sentence.

I can read, write, and spell.

Keys to Legibility Score Box		
Check:	Satisfactory	Needs to Improve
size	☐	☐
shape	☐	☐
slant	☐	☐
spacing	☐	☐
smoothness	☐	☐

Write the sentence.

A picture is a poem

without words.

Keys to Legibility Score Box		
Check:	Satisfactory	Needs to Improve
size	☐	☐
shape	☐	☐
slant	☐	☐
spacing	☐	☐
smoothness		☐

Trace and write.

V   V   V

Vicky

Vivian

Violet

Vera

Vito

Val

Vic sleeps soundly.

Name

Trace and write.

W W W   W

Will

Wendy

Wanda

Ward

Wade

Wes

We played ball.

Trace and write.

Y Y _ _ _ _ _ Y

York

Yates

Yale

Yves

Yvonne

Yvette

Yes, you can.

HIDDEN LETTERS   V W Y

Find these uppercase letters in the picture below.

Trace and write.

K K _ _ _ _ _ K

Kit

Kim

Kay

Ken

Kate

Karl

Kurt bats next.

Trace and write.

X X ‾ ‾ ‾ ‾ ‾ ‾ ‾ ‾ X

Xena

Xavier

Xenia

Xerxes

Xanthe

Xanthus

Xena sings softly.

Trace and write.

Z Z Z _ _ _ _ Z

Zenia

Zora

Zelda

Zeke

Zach

Zena

Zane swings high.

HIDDEN LETTERS V W Y K X Z

Find these uppercase letters in the picture below.

JERI SIMKUS

Write the lowercase letters from **a** to **z**.

Write the lowercase letters from **z** to **a**.

Name

Write the uppercase letters from **A** to **Z**.

Write the uppercase letters from **Z** to **A**.

129

Show students how to draw these figures, beginning with the letterforms.

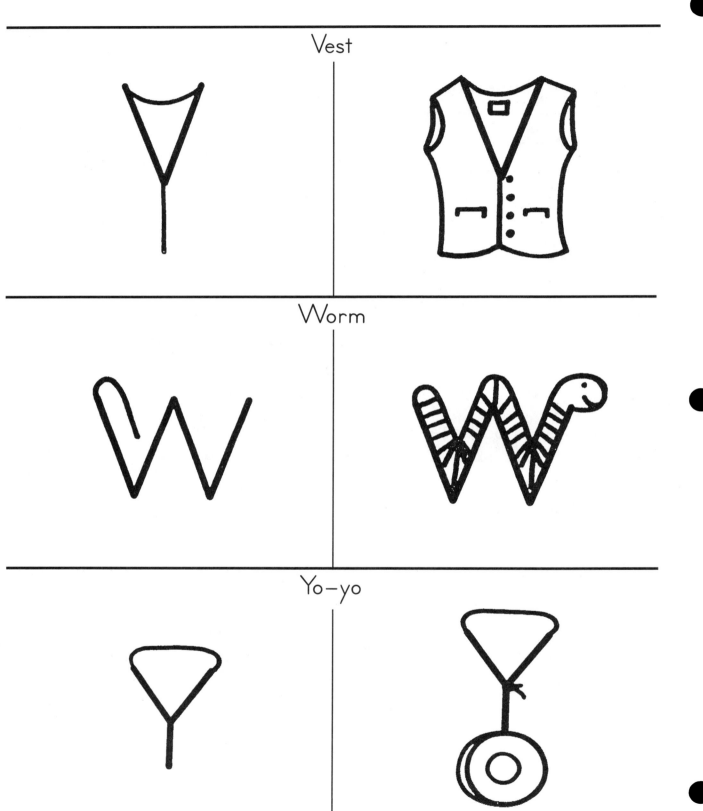

Vest

Worm

Yo-yo

Show students how to draw these figures, beginning with the letterforms.

Kites

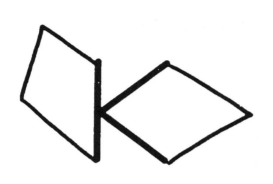 

X marks the spot

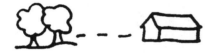 

Zipper

131

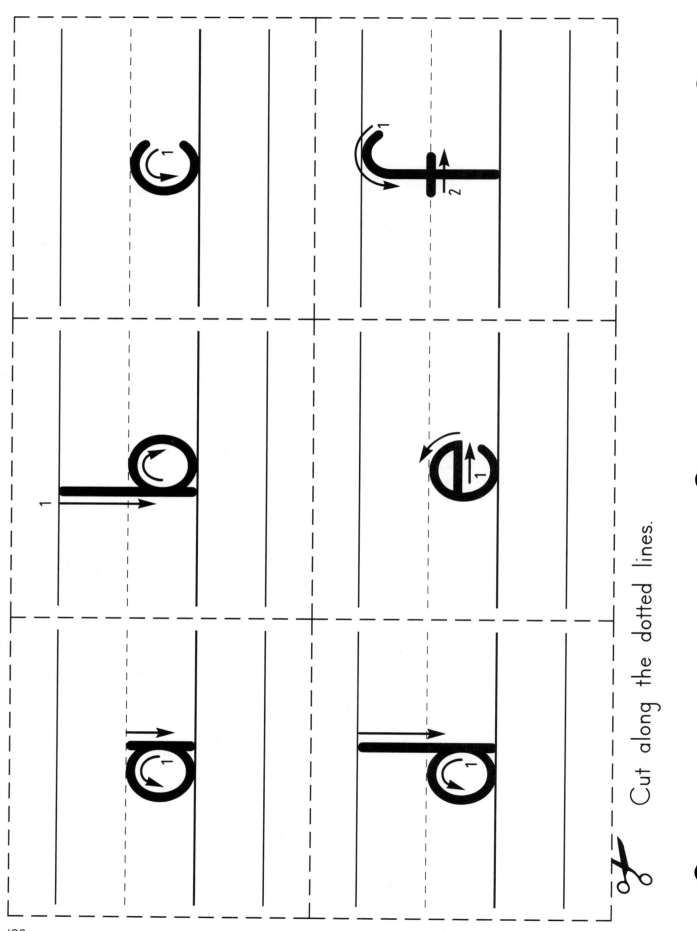

Cut along the dotted lines.

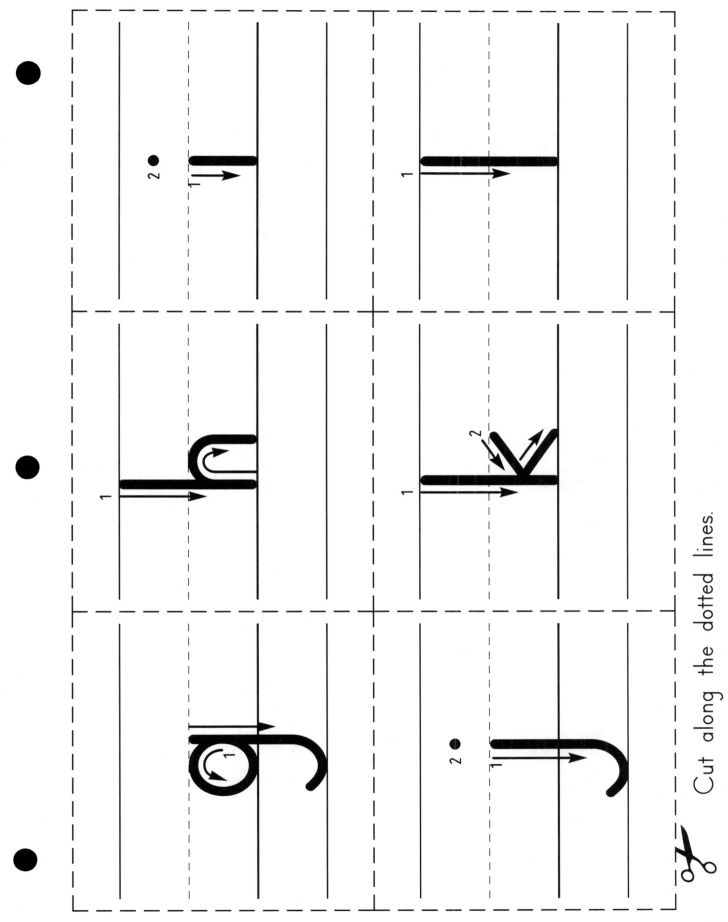

Cut along the dotted lines.

133

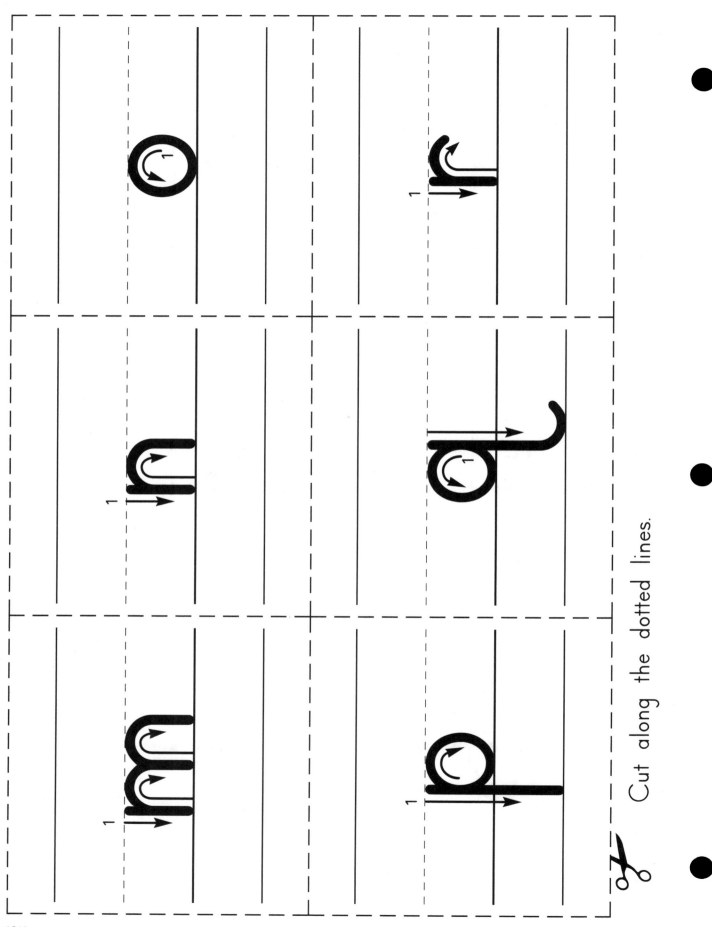

Cut along the dotted lines.

134

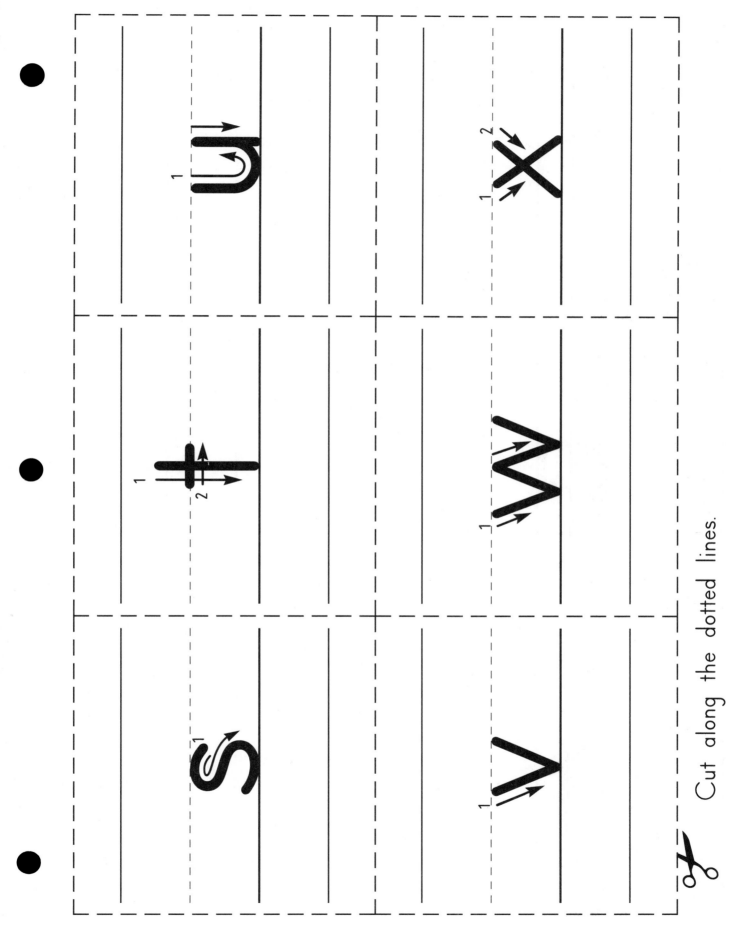

Cut along the dotted lines.

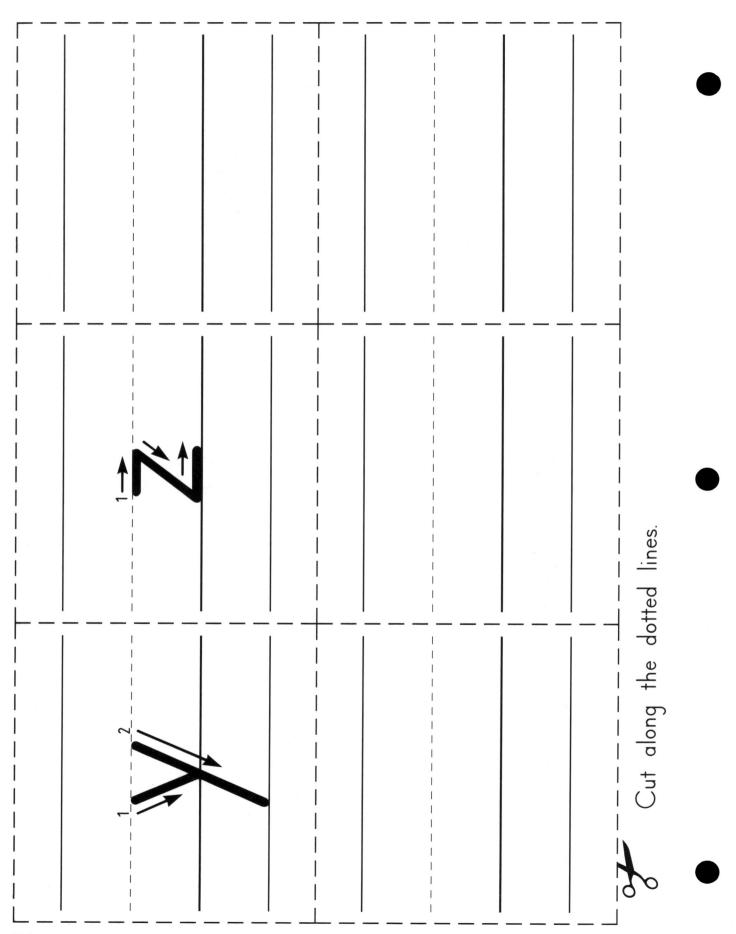

Cut along the dotted lines.

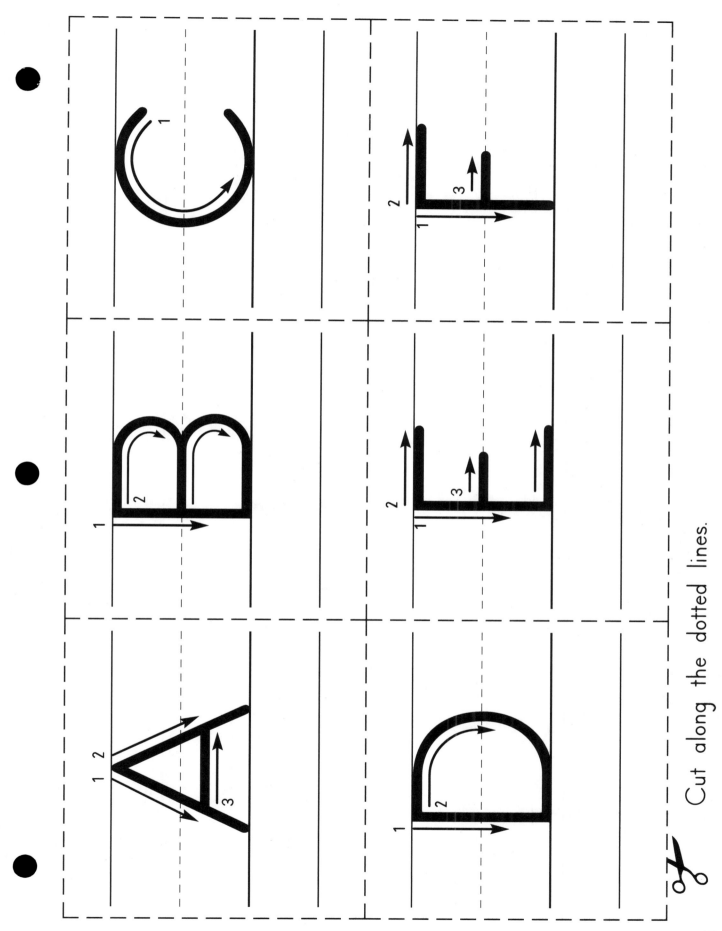

Cut along the dotted lines.

137

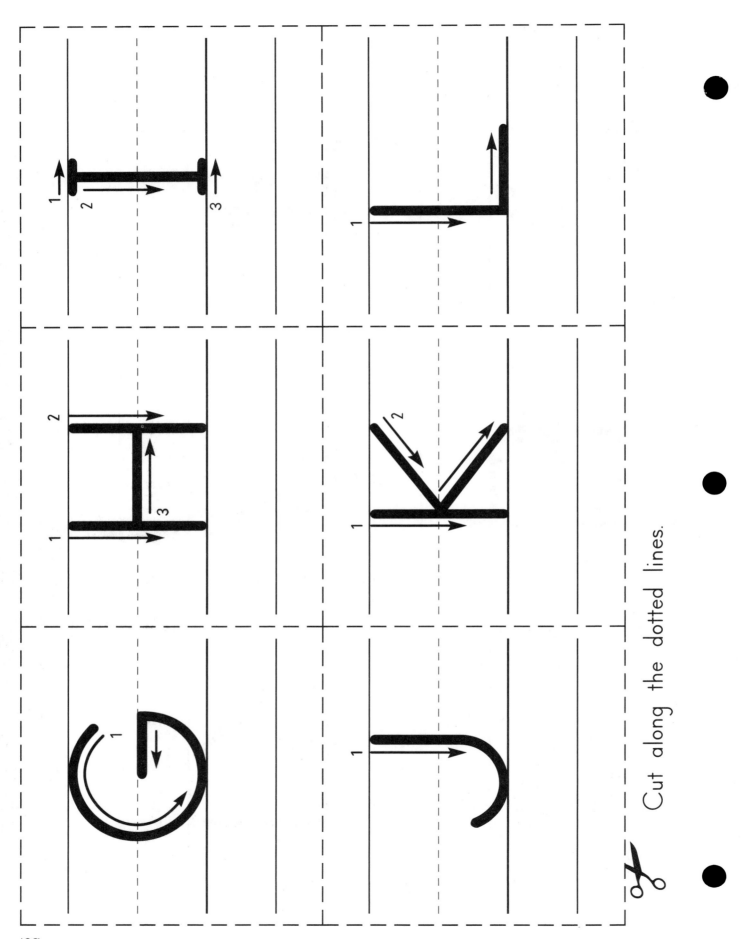

Cut along the dotted lines.

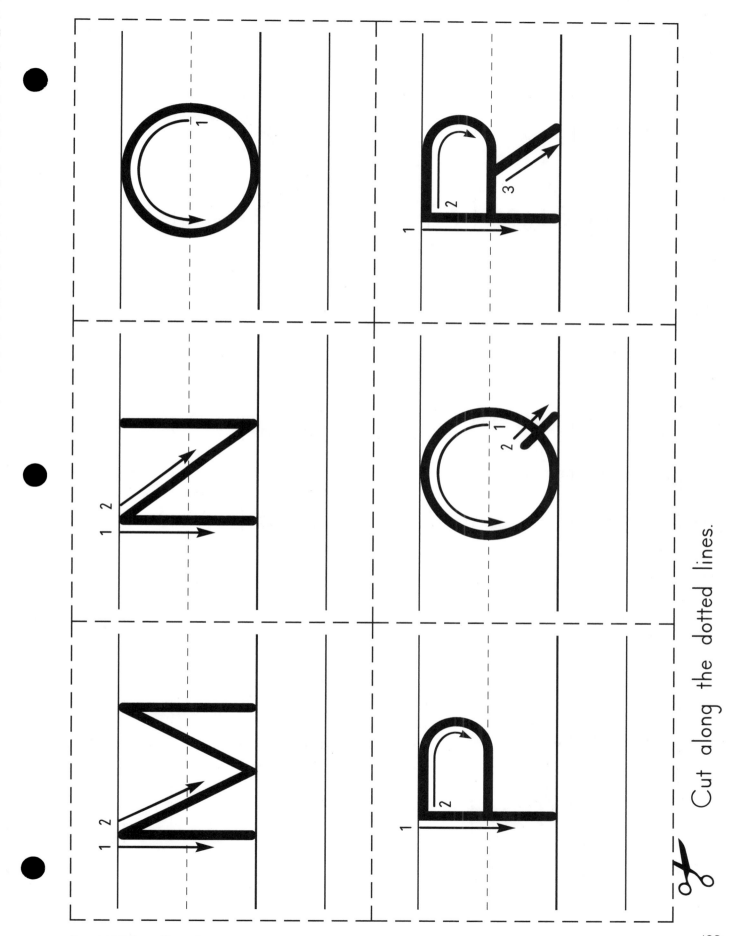

Cut along the dotted lines.

Cut along the dotted lines.

140

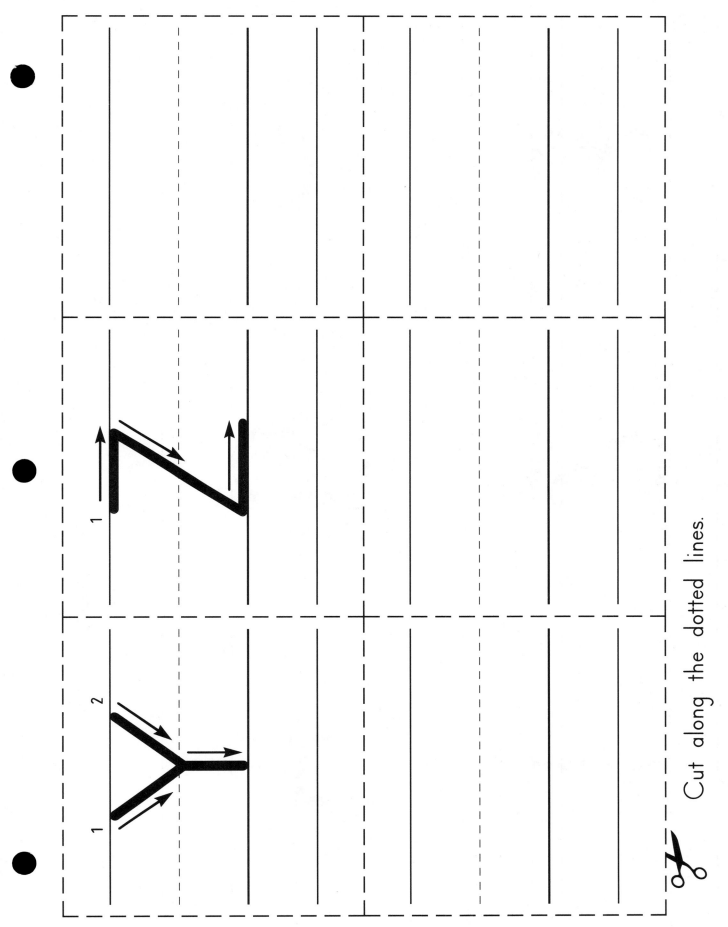

Cut along the dotted lines.

141

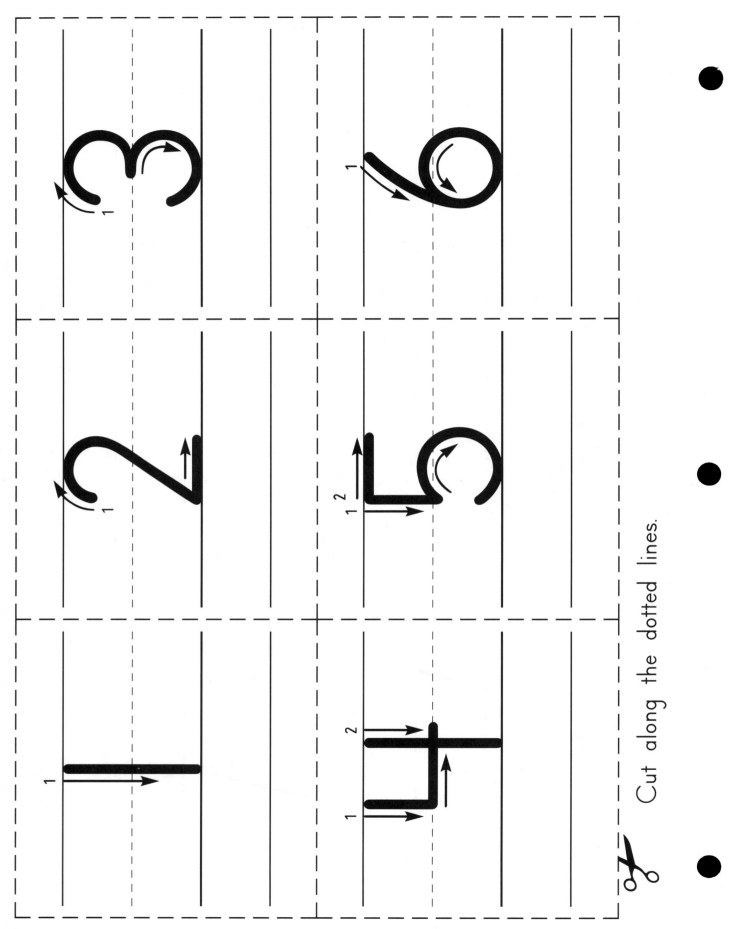

Cut along the dotted lines.

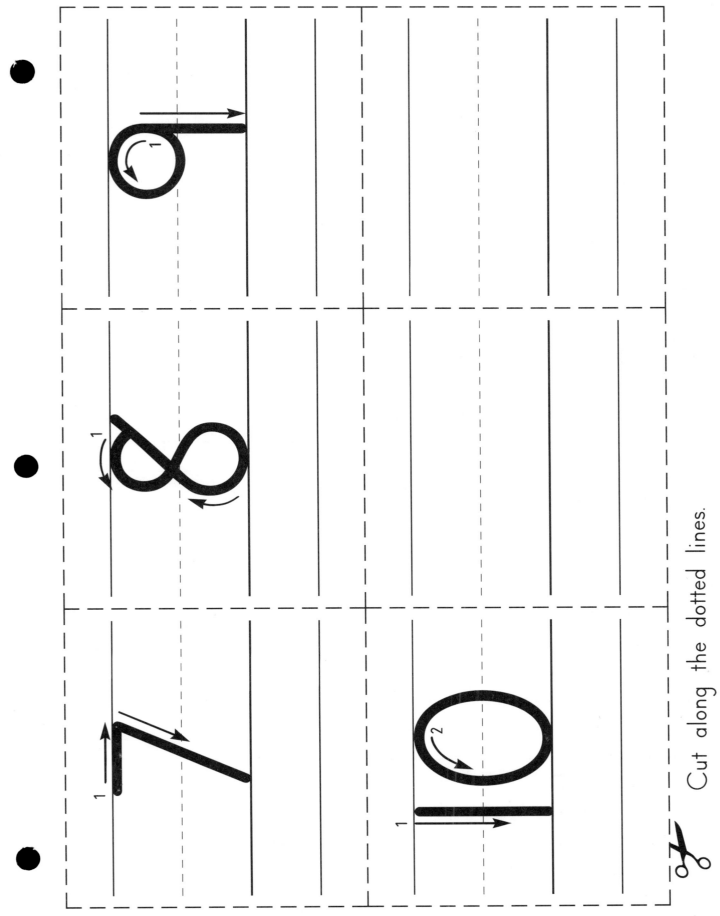

Cut along the dotted lines.

143